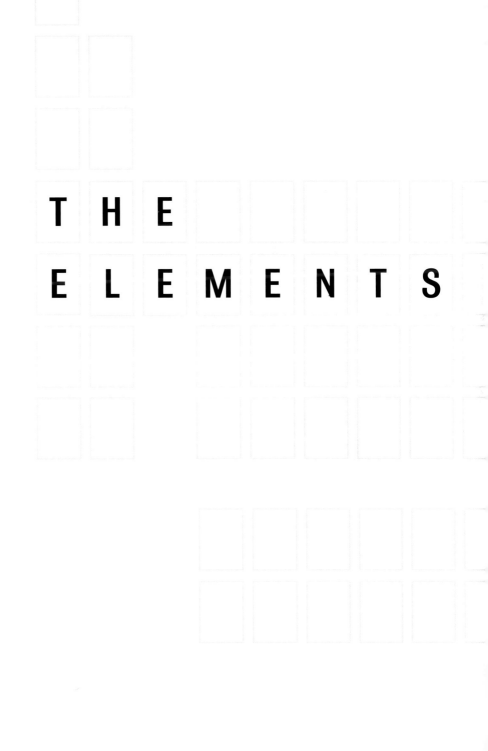

THE ELEMENTS

Quarto is the authority on a wide range of topics.

Quarto educates, entertains and enriches the lives of
our readers—enthusiasts and lovers of hands-on living.

www.QuartoKnows.com

Published by Quad Books
Copyright © 2017 Quid Publishing
Conceived, designed and produced by
Quid Publishing
an imprint of The Quarto Group
Level One
Ovest House
58 West Street
Brighton
BN1 2RA
England

ISBN: 978–0–85762–505-2

Design by Lindsey Johns

Printed in China

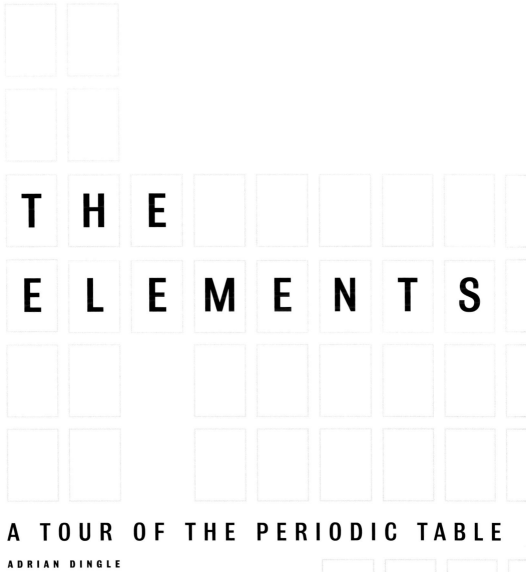

THE ELEMENTS

A TOUR OF THE PERIODIC TABLE

ADRIAN DINGLE

QUAD BOOKS

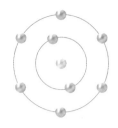

Contents

Introduction   6

H   Hydrogen   10

Alkali metals   12

Li   Lithium   14
Na   Sodium   16
K   Potassium   18
Rb   Rubidium   20
Cs   Caesium   22
Fr   Francium   24

Alkaline earth metals   26

Be   Beryllium   28
Mg   Magnesium   30
Ca   Calcium   32
Sr   Strontium   34
Ba   Barium   36
Ra   Radium   38

Transition metals   40

Sc   Scandium   42
Ti   Titanium   44
V   Vanadium   46
Cr   Chromium   48
Mn   Manganese   50
Fe   Iron   52
Co   Cobalt   54
Ni   Nickel   56
Cu   Copper   58
Zn   Zinc   60
Y   Yttrium   62
Zr   Zirconium   64
Nb   Niobium   66
Mo   Molybdenum   68
Tc   Technetium   70
Ru   Ruthenium   72
Rh   Rhodium   74
Pd   Palladium   76
Ag   Silver   78
Cd   Cadmium   80
Hf   Hafnium   82
Ta   Tantalum   84
W   Tungsten   86
Re   Rhenium   88
Os   Osmium   90
Ir   Iridium   92
Pt   Platinum   94
Au   Gold   96
Hg   Mercury   98

Post-transition metals   100

Al   Aluminium   102
Ga   Gallium   104
In   Indium   106
Sn   Tin   108
Tl   Thallium   110
Pb   Lead   112
Bi   Bismuth   114

Bismuth, p. 114

Metalloids 116

B	Boron	118
Si	Silicon	120
Ge	Germanium	122
As	Arsenic	124
Sb	Antimony	126
Te	Tellurium	128
Po	Polonium	130

Ruthenium, p. 72

Lanthanoids 132

La	Lanthanum	134
Ce	Cerium	136
Pr	Praseodymium	138
Nd	Neodymium	140
Pm	Promethium	142
Sm	Samarium	144
Eu	Europium	146
Gd	Gadolinium	148
Tb	Terbium	150
Dy	Dysprosium	152
Ho	Holmium	154
Er	Erbium	156
Tm	Thulium	158
Yb	Ytterbium	160
Lu	Lutetium	162

Actinoids 164

Ac	Actinium	166
Th	Thorium	168
Pa	Protactinum	170
U	Uranium	172
Pu	Plutonium	174
Cm	Curium	176

Non-metals 178

C	Carbon	180
N	Nitrogen	182
O	Oxygen	184
P	Phosphorus	186
S	Sulfur	188
Se	Selenium	190

Halogens 192

F	Fluorine	194
Cl	Chlorine	196
Br	Bromine	198
I	Iodine	200
At	Astatine	202

Noble gases 204

He	Helium	206
Ne	Neon	208
Ar	Argon	210
Kr	Krypton	212
Xe	Xenon	214
Rn	Radon	216

Glossary	218
Index	220
Credits	224

Introduction

'Stuff', or more scientifically speaking, matter, is everywhere. If something takes up space and has mass, then it is matter. That's a pretty diverse group of things that, on the face of it, don't appear to have much in common with one another – however, they are much more alike than you may imagine. All matter is composed of some basic building blocks; more precisely, 118 building blocks, which when arranged in an infinite number of ways produce that matter.

The history of these building blocks is as diverse as their properties, ranging from discovery stories that are lost in the mist of ancient times, to ones that have only been officially confirmed and named very recently. They also have an incredibly diverse set of characteristics (physical and chemical properties) of their own, each with a unique place in the grand scheme. What are these building blocks that we speak of? They are more commonly known as the elements.

▶ *All matter is composed of some combination of the 118 chemical elements that are currently recognised and named.*

Ordering the elements

The 118 elements are corralled and called to order in one of the most iconic symbols of science of all time: the periodic table. Whole books have been devoted to the history and development of the table, and like almost all scientific endeavours, its evolution can be attributed to the work of many people. The person usually considered the 'father' of the periodic table is the Russian chemist Dmitri Mendeleev (1834–1907), but many others preceded his genius. Similarly, since Mendeleev's first table of 1869, many more have built upon his work to get us to the modern IUPAC (International Union of Pure and Applied Chemistry) table that we use today. Mendeleev's successors include those who spearheaded the development of the atomic model in the late nineteenth and early twentieth centuries, such as Dane Niels Bohr (1885–1962), Austrian Erwin Schrödinger (1887–1961), Englishman J. J. Thomson (1856–1940), New Zealander Ernest Rutherford (1871–1937), Englishman James Chadwick (1891–1974) and Frenchman Louis de Broglie (1892–1987), along with incredibly important (but generally less well known) contributions from many others. Henry Moseley (1887–1915) is one such person, and his contribution marked a profound change in terms of the way that the elements on the periodic table were ordered.

Discovering the atomic number

In Mendeleev's original table the elements were ordered by their atomic weights. This was an idea that persisted with him, to the point of his 'explaining away' some apparent anomalies. For example, in Mendeleev's table tellurium and iodine were 'incorrectly' ordered, with the heavier Te (number 52) coming before the lighter I (number 53) in his scheme. At the time, Mendeleev said that the atomic weights of either one (or both) of these elements had been incorrectly calculated, thus explaining the break in his sequence.

It took experiments by Moseley in 1913 – building on earlier work by Anton van den Broek (1870–1926) – to make more sense of the apparent anomaly caused by Mendeleev's ordering. Moseley determined that elements, when struck with an incident energy source, emitted X-rays. When he conducted the same experiment on fourteen of the elements known at the time, he found a mathematical relationship between the X-rays and the square of an integer that represented the element's position on the table. What Moseley had done was to discover what we know now as the atomic number, and it is by atomic number that the periodic table is now ordered.

Moseley's work also had at least one other important impact on the periodic table. Since his experiments accurately determined the positions of the known elements, they also allowed chemists to see that elements were missing from the sequence, thus allowing them to target their searches for new

KEY FIGURE

DMITRI MENDELEEV

1834–1907

The Russian chemist Dmitri Mendeleev is the pivotal figure in the history of the periodic table, as he was the first to propose an organization of elements that resembles the modern-day table. In truth, important work by many other scientists had preceded Mendeleev, but the Russian's ordering of all of the elements by atomic weights revealed patterns that are still relevant and familiar today. His table of 1869 also left gaps that allowed for the prediction of, at the time, undiscovered elements.

⊙ *Mendeleev's original periodic organization was first published in 1869. The letter 'J' represents the element iodine.*

		Ti = 50	Zr = 90	? = 180
		V = 51	Nb = 94	Ta = 182
		Cr = 52	Mo = 96	W = 186
		Mn = 55	Rh = 104,4	Pt = 197,4
		Fe = 56	Ru = 104,4	Ir = 198
	Ni = Co = 59	Pd = 106,6	Os = 199
		Cu = 63,4	Ag = 108	Hg = 200
H = 1		Zn = 65,2	Cd = 112	
	Be = 9,4	Mg = 24	? = 68	Ur = 116	Au = 197 ?
	B = 11	Al = 27,4	? = 70	Sn = 118	
	C = 12	Si = 28	As = 75	Sb = 122	Bi = 210 ?
	N = 14	P = 31	Se = 79,4	Te = 128 ?	
	O = 16	S = 32	Br = 80	J = 127	
Li = 7	F = 19	Na = 23	Cl = 35,5	Rb = 85,4	Cs = 133	Tl = 204
		K = 39	Sr = 87,6	Ba = 137	Pb = 207
		Ca = 40	Ce = 92	
		? = 45	La = 94	
		?Er = 56	Di = 95	
		?Yt = 60	Th = 118 ?	
		?In = 75,6		

⊛ *The control room of the Bevatron particle accelerator in 1960. The experiments of the Nuclear Age led to the discovery of the manmade elements.*

elements more specifically. These targeted searches led to the discovery of seven 'missing' elements within the first ninety-two, namely those with atomic numbers of 43, 61, 72, 75, 85, 87, and 91. Promethium, number 61, would be the final of these seven elements to be discovered, in 1945.

Manmade elements

When we turn our attention to the elements with atomic numbers greater than 92, we come to the next stage of development of the periodic table, the manmade elements. These elements were each born out of the Nuclear Age, where scientists crashed relatively light nuclei into one other, either in particle accelerators or nuclear bombs, and where careful analysis of the products of these collisions allowed the isolation of new, heavier nuclei. Pioneers of this work include Americans Al Ghiorso (1915–2010) and Glenn Seaborg (1912–1999), and Russians Georgy Flyorov (1913–1990)

and Yuri Oganessian (b. 1933). Seaborg and Oganessian are distinguished in at least one way from all other scientists that ever contributed to the development of the periodic table, since, depending on exactly how one defines naming, they are the only two people to have had elements named after them while they were still alive – seaborgium was named in 1997 when Seaborg was 85 years old, and oganesson was named in 2016 when Oganessian was 83.

Periods and 'families'

The periodic table does far more than simply gather the elements into a single, handy reference guide; it also organises them. The specific arrangement of the elements is incredibly important, since the rows (known as periods) and columns (known as groups) are not randomly generated – rather, each horizontal and vertical relationship hides a deeper, more profound meaning of chemical similarity and subtle difference. Meaningful chemistry without reference to the periodic table is close to impossible. The modern periodic table now boasts 118 officially recognised and named elements, with the first seven periods complete. Each space on the table shows the element's atomic number, its symbol and its average atomic weight. Elements in the same group tend to show many similar physical and chemical properties, and as such are sometimes called 'families'. Elements in any given period show gradual changes as the periodic table is traversed, with similarities often seen between adjacent elements, but with significant differences being apparent once one has crossed the whole table. These general similarities are not without their

▼ *The modern IUPAC periodic table, consisting of 118 chemical elements, including the recent formal additions of elements with atomic numbers 113, 115, 117, and 118, which complete the seventh period.*

1																	18
1 H	2											13	14	15	16	17	2 He
3 Li	4 Be											5 B	6 C	7 N	8 O	9 F	10 Ne
11 Na	12 Mg	3	4	5	6	7	8	9	10	11	12	13 Al	14 Si	15 P	16 S	17 Cl	18 Ar
19 K	20 Ca	21 Sc	22 Ti	23 V	24 Cr	25 Mn	26 Fe	27 Co	28 Ni	29 Cu	30 Zn	31 Ga	32 Ge	33 As	34 Se	35 Br	36 Kr
37 Rb	38 Sr	39 Y	40 Zr	41 Nb	42 Mo	43 Tc	44 Ru	45 Rh	46 Pd	47 Ag	48 Cd	49 In	50 Sn	51 Sb	52 Te	53 I	54 Xe
55 Cs	56 Ba	57–71	72 Hf	73 Ta	74 W	75 Re	76 Os	77 Ir	78 Pt	79 Au	80 Hg	81 Tl	82 Pb	83 Bi	84 Po	85 At	86 Rn
87 Fr	88 Ra	89–103	104 Rf	105 Db	106 Sg	107 Bh	108 Hs	109 Mt	110 Ds	111 Rg	112 Cn	113 Nh	114 Fl	115 Mc	116 Lv	117 Ts	118 Og

57 La	58 Ce	59 Pr	60 Nd	61 Pm	62 Sm	63 Eu	64 Gd	65 Tb	66 Dy	67 Ho	68 Er	69 Tm	70 Yb	71 Lu
89 Ac	90 Th	91 Pa	92 U	93 Np	94 Pu	95 Am	96 Cm	97 Bk	98 Cf	99 Es	100 Fm	101 Md	102 No	103 Lr

own anomalies and interruptions, of course, but no matter, the periodic table still provides both chemistry neophytes and seasoned chemical geniuses with profoundly important information about the ragtag collection of unique substances that we call the elements.

This book aims to give a broad overview of the diversity of the elements for a general audience, and as such it is not overly technical. Any book about the elements has to consider both its scope (which elements to omit if there is insufficient space for all 118, as here), and how to present them. There is, of course, more than one way to do this (alphabetically, collected by group, chronologically according to date of discovery), and each method has its pros and cons. I have opted for a flexible approach that allows for groups to be represented (e.g., the halogens and noble gases), alongside larger,

Alkali metals
Alkaline earth metals
Transition metals
Post-transition metals
Metalloids
Lanthanoids
Actinoids
Non-metals
Halogens
Noble gases
Other

less well-defined collections (e.g., metalloids and post-transition metals). In this way, it is entirely acceptable to highlight uniqueness, and in fact the first element in this book is a good example of that. Element number 1, hydrogen, is a tricky element to pin down in many ways, and it is with it that we start out our elemental journey.

Hydrogen

Chemical symbol	H
Atomic number	1
Atomic mass	1.008
Boiling point	−252.879 °C (−423.182 °F)
Melting point	−259.16 °C (−434.49 °F)

Hydrogen is the most abundant element in the universe – it makes up 88 percent of all the atoms present, with helium coming in a distant second at 11 percent. More often than not you'll find it placed above lithium in the periodic table, at the head of group 1 in period 1. Indeed, the official IUPAC periodic table assigns hydrogen that position, but as a gas and not a highly reactive metal, its placement is certainly open to debate.

An exceptional element

Hydrogen atoms only contain a single electron. This makes hydrogen a tricky element to categorise. Should the superlight, colourless gas sit with the silver-coloured, solid metals of group 1 that also have just one valence electron? Probably not. What about treating hydrogen like a group 17 element, as these, like hydrogen, only require one more electron to complete their valence shell? Either way there are physical and chemical contradictions, so element number 1 is often treated as an exceptional entity.

Water-forming

Discovered by Henry Cavendish (1731–1810) in 1766, hydrogen was tantalisingly close to being discovered long before the English eccentric managed to correctly identify it as a unique substance. A number of prominent chemists had described flammable 'airs' that were almost certainly hydrogen, notably Robert Boyle (1627–1691). However, partly because real chemical analysis was in its infancy at the time, and partly because one needs a little luck to discover an element, hydrogen went formally undiscovered for decades prior to Cavendish's definitive experiments.

⊲ Atomic hydrogen is the most abundant element in the universe, present in space in stars and in the most important star for earth, the sun.

Electron configuration: 1.
The most common isotope of H
has only one proton and only
one electron.

He christened element number 1 by
demonstrating that when hydrogen burns it
forms water – hence 'hydrogen', from the
Greek *hydro* and *genes*, meaning 'water'
and 'forming', respectively.

The flammability that Cavendish
demonstrated has been both a blessing and
a curse in the history of hydrogen. The
Hindenburg disaster was one of its spectacular
failures, when, in 1937, a hydrogen-filled
airship exploded in a ball of fire in the New
Jersey night sky, killing thirty-six people.
Hydrogen was used in early airships as the
'lifting gas' since its density is approximately
only $1/14$ that of air, and its presence therefore
creates the buoyancy needed for the aircraft to
rise. On the plus side, colourless and odourless
H_2 gas has enormous promise as an alternative
energy source, since when it burns, it only
produces harmless water, making it a zero-
emission fuel.

Both water and acid

As the chief component of the sun and stars,
and as two-thirds of the atoms that make up a
water molecule, hydrogen is vital to earth's very
survival. However, it is in the form of its ion,
H^+, that hydrogen has a huge impact on
everyday life. When H^+ ions combine with
water molecules to form H_3O^+ (hydronium)
ions, they produce an acidic solution. These
substances, and their chemical opposites, bases,
are crucially important both in industrial

Ⓐ *One of the best known and most
spectacular examples of the flammability of
hydrogen is encapsulated in the* Hindenburg
(a German passenger airship) disaster of 1937.

settings and in our homes. A compound such
as sulfuric acid, for example, is used extensively
in the manufacture of many chemicals (see
sulfur, pp. 188–89), whereas other acids and
bases, like lemon juice, battery acid, vinegar,
cleaning products and over-the-counter
medicines (indigestion remedies, for example),
play an important role in everyday life.

Alkali metals

The six elements that comprise the first column (group 1) on the far left of the periodic table are collectively known as the alkali metals. Lithium, sodium, potassium, rubidium, caesium and francium are sometimes joined by hydrogen at the head of the group, but as we have seen, hydrogen is a unique element, and it is considered by some as being placed there purely for convenience, rather than belonging to the group with any conviction.

On the following pages:

Li	Lithium	Rb	Rubidium
Na	Sodium	Cs	Caesium
K	Potassium	Fr	Francium

1 H																	2 He
3 Li	4 Be											5 B	6 C	7 N	8 O	9 F	10 Ne
11 Na	12 Mg											13 Al	14 Si	15 P	16 S	17 Cl	18 Ar
19 K	20 Ca	21 Sc	22 Ti	23 V	24 Cr	25 Mn	26 Fe	27 Co	28 Ni	29 Cu	30 Zn	31 Ga	32 Ge	33 As	34 Se	35 Br	36 Kr
37 Rb	38 Sr	39 Y	40 Zr	41 Nb	42 Mo	43 Tc	44 Ru	45 Rh	46 Pd	47 Ag	48 Cd	49 In	50 Sn	51 Sb	52 Te	53 I	54 Xe
55 Cs	56 Ba	57–71	72 Hf	73 Ta	74 W	75 Re	76 Os	77 Ir	78 Pt	79 Au	80 Hg	81 Tl	82 Pb	83 Bi	84 Po	85 At	86 Rn
87 Fr	88 Ra	89–103	104 Rf	105 Db	106 Sg	107 Bh	108 Hs	109 Mt	110 Ds	111 Rg	112 Cn	113 Nh	114 Fl	115 Mc	116 Lv	117 Ts	118 Og

57 La	58 Ce	59 Pr	60 Nd	61 Pm	62 Sm	63 Eu	64 Gd	65 Tb	66 Dy	67 Ho	68 Er	69 Tm	70 Yb	71 Lu
89 Ac	90 Th	91 Pa	92 U	93 Np	94 Pu	95 Am	96 Cm	97 Bk	98 Cf	99 Es	100 Fm	101 Md	102 No	103 Lr

Violent reactions

The alkali metals are noted for their reactivity, which is due to the ease with which they lose their single valence electron, forming the more stable +1 ion in the process. Their reactivity is extreme when compared to other metals. For example, they will react immediately with the oxygen when exposed to air, and react violently when they come into contact with water.

The reaction with oxygen can be seen when these soft metals are cut with a knife. One will see an unsullied, shiny surface at the point of the cut, because the internal atoms of the metal have been protected from oxygen. However, once exposed, the bright silvery colour will dull within seconds, as an oxide layer is built up on the surface of the exposed metal.

Reactions of the group 1 metals with water are equally visible. As particularly light metals, small pieces of them will float on the surface of water and appear to dance around as hydrogen gas is liberated from the water. These reactions are exothermic (ones that release energy), and often the energy released is sufficient to ignite the hydrogen gas and produce what looks like a 'floating fire' on the surface of the water – spectacular!

Body matters

In their compounds, sodium and potassium in particular have crucial roles in human biology in determining electrical impulses and movement of water in the body. Lithium compounds have proved to be vital medicines in the field of mental illness, being used as antidepressants and mood modifiers.

▶ The group 1 metals are typified by their reactivity, which increases down the group. They react with water to produce gaseous hydrogen that is ignited in the exothermic process.

Li Lithium

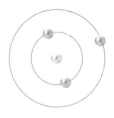

Electron configuration: 2.1

Chemical symbol	Li
Atomic number	3
Atomic mass	6.94
Boiling point	1342 °C (2448 °F)
Melting point	180.50 °C (356.97 °F)

The lightest of all of the group 1 elements, lithium exhibits many typical properties of the alkali metal family: it is light, soft and reactive. If somebody is said to be 'on lithium', it generally means that they are receiving a lithium-based medication prescribed for a mental disorder. As such, lithium is sometimes seen in a negative light. Of course, for the patient receiving the stabilising medication, this may be far from the truth.

Lithium rocks

The Swedish chemist Johan August Arfvedson (1792–1841) eventually discovered lithium in 1817. 'Eventually', since this was not before a number of earlier chemists had come close to identifying a new element contained within certain rocks. Lithium is found in a number of naturally occurring minerals, notably spodumene and petalite. Several early chemists had suspicions of there being a new element present in these minerals, but it took an analysis of petalite by Arfvedson to confirm it. Lithium's proliferation in such minerals is reflected in its name, which comes from the Greek *lithos*, meaning 'stone'.

The manic element

It took almost another century and a half before the Australian psychiatrist John Cade (1912–1980) first championed lithium's use as an antidepressant in 1949. His initial experiments with rodents suggested that lithium carbonate could be used as an effective mood stabiliser. Within about twenty years, the use of the carbonate had exploded as a treatment for bipolar disorder in humans, with generally excellent results. Lithium carbonate is still a popular medicine today.

◀ *The Swedish chemist J. A. Arfvedson discovered lithium in 1817, during an analysis of a sample of the naturally occurring mineral petalite.*

Lightweight highflier

As the lightest of all the known metals, lithium has found a major use in metal alloys. Its use here is usually directly related to its light weight and the subsequent reduction in mass that it offers. There are obvious advantages in the aerospace industry, and aluminium–lithium alloys form part of many commercial aircraft. They are also used in the *Falcon 9* space rocket made by SpaceX, the ambitious commercial space-travel company founded by the entrepreneur Elon Musk (b. 1971).

In consumer products, 'lithium' batteries have proved extremely popular. Here lithium acts as the anode (the negative pole in a cell), readily releasing electrons in a typical group 1 manner. In applications where mass is an issue,

Ⓐ *Aluminium–lithium alloy tanks contain liquid oxygen and rocket-grade kerosene, the propellants for the* Falcon 9 *spacecraft that has been designed and manufactured by the private US company SpaceX.*

especially in small, portable personal devices such as watches, lithium's light weight offers a huge advantage. Lithium batteries can also exhibit very long lives when compared to other cells, and the combination of lightness and long life often means that despite their relatively expensive nature, they are preferred. Their long life is also utilised in surgically implanted medical devices such as pacemakers, where a need for frequent replacement would be extremely inconvenient.

Ⓐ *Lithium is used in many types of batteries, including these 'button' cells, which are often used to power small devices such as watches.*

Na Sodium

Chemical symbol	Na
Atomic number	11
Atomic mass	22.990
Boiling point	882.940 °C (1621.292 °F)
Melting point	97.794 °C (208.029 °F)

A ubiquitous element when considering compounds, sodium is paradoxically elusive when it comes to its pure, metallic state. As a typical member of group 1, sodium *the element* is keen to lose its singular outer electron to achieve a more energetically stable electronic structure. The propensity to achieve this more stable state is so strong that sodium will react with almost anything that it comes into contact with.

KEY FIGURE

HUMPHRY DAVY

1778–1829

Humphry Davy was a British chemist and a pioneer in the field of electrochemistry – the study of the relationship between electrical and chemical phenomena. Davy discovered sodium in 1807. By passing electricity through sodium hydroxide, he managed to separate the element sodium from the compound, in a process known as electrolysis. Davy discovered potassium in the same way and in the same year, and isolated calcium, strontium, barium and magnesium the following year via a similar method.

Exothermic reaction

Sodium's tendency to react is so strong that the soft, silvery, putty-like metal, which can be cut with a knife, is normally stored under oil to prevent even its reaction with air. Its reaction with water is a rapid one that produces the flammable gas hydrogen. This reaction generates heat, and if a large enough piece of

◁ *Sodium reacts vigorously with water. Here, the energy released in the exothermic reaction is sufficient to cause an explosion.*

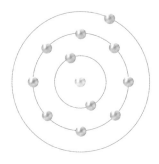

'[The substance produced] from soda, which was fluid in the degree of heat of the alkali during its formation, became solid on cooling, and appeared having the lustre of silver.'

—excerpt from Humphy Davy's original paper of 1807, detailing his isolation of sodium

Electron configuration: 2.8.1

sodium is used then the energy produced can cause the hydrogen gas to catch fire. (Indeed, sodium's vigorous reaction with water is a classic chemistry demonstration that has been witnessed by generations of schoolchildren.)

Ion regulator

Whenever it does react, sodium metal loses one negative electron and forms its positive ion, Na^+. In this state, sodium finds relative stability, and it will remain benign in common compounds such as sodium chloride (common salt). It is in its ionic state that sodium operates in the human body. As an essential element, sodium ions help regulate the movement of water across the membranes of human cells, and as such are an integral part of many biological functions including that of the kidneys.

Lighting the way

A far more visible application of sodium is its use in street lighting. Small amounts of solid sodium metal are encased in tubes along with neon and tiny percentages of group 18 elements (see pp. 204–216). As the sodium is gradually heated in the lamp, it vaporises, and as it does, the movement of electrons within the sodium atoms creates the characteristic yellow light. The wavelength of the light produced in this way is found to be effective in outdoor applications, particularly when fog is present.

▶ *The familiar yellow glow of street lighting is due to the sodium vapor in the lamps generating light of a wavelength equal to 589 nm, which is in the yellow part of the visible spectrum.*

K Potassium

Chemical symbol	K
Atomic number	19
Atomic mass	39.098
Boiling point	1398 °F (759 °C)
Melting point	146.3 °F (63.5 °C)

⊙ Potassium metal will react violently with water to yield a solution of potassium hydroxide and hydrogen gas. The reaction releases sufficient energy for the hydrogen to ignite.

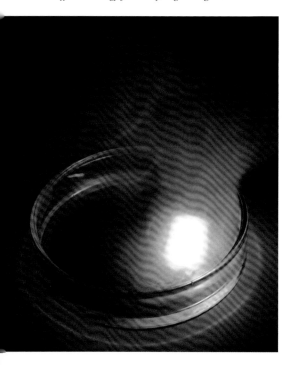

Culturally, potassium is often associated with bananas, since they contain a large amount of the element. There are, however, plenty of other foods that contain larger amounts of potassium, including potatoes, spinach and some beans. Really, though, it doesn't matter how potassium is consumed, as long as it is! It is one of life's essential elements and crucial to our wellbeing.

As a soft, shiny metal, potassium resembles sodium both in appearance and in many of its properties. Another quintessential group 1 element, it will react instantaneously with oxygen and violently with water. Potassium and sodium were essentially 'born together' when Humphry Davy perfected the art of electrolysis. This means that sodium and potassium are essentially 'twins', but their simultaneous discovery illustrates a far more important point about the nature of the periodic table. When elements are in the same group, their properties are often very similar. When they are adjacent, that similarity can be amplified, so their appearance together is not a coincidence – it occurs because they are so alike. Davy named his newly found element after the substance that he had extracted it from, and that he knew as 'potash'. The particular potash that he used, we now know as potassium hydroxide. Potash also holds the key to potassium's chemical symbol, K, which always seems somewhat exotic, but is easily explained when one knows that the Latin for potash is *kalium*.

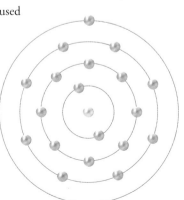

Potash evaporation ponds, such as this one at a mine in Utah, are used to isolate potassium-containing potash. The sun evaporates the water, leaving behind crystallised potassium salts.

Life and death

The similarity between elements 11 and 19 is also evident in the human body, where potassium – in its ionic form, K^+ – plays a similar role to sodium. The regulation of the electrical signals that determine nerve function is just one way in which potassium is an essential element for life.

Ironically, potassium continues to be a component of one of the chemicals used to execute humans by lethal injection in those countries where capital punishment still exists. As the third of three drugs administered, potassium chloride is injected to stop the heart after the prisoner has been sedated and paralysed by other substances.

Back to life

Potassium, again in its ionic form, K^+, controls many of the growth processes in plants. Just as the element helps to regulate water flow in humans, a similar role is found in plants, where potassium is central to the process of photosynthesis that converts sunlight into energy. Because of this, potassium is used to improve the general physical quality of vegetation. A huge percentage of the potassium that is produced in the modern world is used to make various potassium-based fertilisers, such as potassium nitrate and potassium sulfate.

Electron configuration:
2.8.8.1

Rb Rubidium

Chemical symbol	Rb
Atomic number	37
Atomic mass	85.468
Boiling point	688 °C (1270 °F)
Melting point	39.30 °C (102.74 °F)

Rubidium is often found alongside potassium in naturally occurring minerals in the earth's crust, but, like potassium, because of its reactivity, rubidium is never found as the free metal. Despite its name – which derives from the Latin for deepest red, *rubidius* – rubidium isn't actually red; rather, it is named after the bright red lines that were observed in its visible spectrum.

As we make our way down group 1 to the fifth period, the metals are starting to get a little menacing. As we have seen, the group 1 elements are characterised by their reactivity, and the tendency to react increases as the group is descended. Not only does rubidium react violently with water, it has a nasty habit of spontaneously igniting in air. As noted above, rubidium's name is linked to its discovery, in 1861, by Robert Bunsen (1811–1899) (inventor of the Bunsen burner), and his collaborator, Gustav R. Kirchhoff (1824–1887). Along with caesium, rubidium was one of the first two elements discovered using a spectroscope. Bunsen and Kirchhoff had invented the apparatus in 1859, and before long it had led to the discovery of two new elements. The spectroscope allowed light from a mineral source to be analysed, and from the unique spectral lines that were observed, new elements could be identified.

Nearly another liquid metal

The melting point of rubidium is only 39 °C (103 °F), so holding a piece of the metal in your hand would be sufficient to turn the silvery-white mass into a liquid. Of course, doing so would be foolish, since the metal would react with the moisture on your hand, and you would have a nasty problem involving the production of flammable hydrogen gas!

◀ *Gustav R. Kirchhoff using an early three-arm spectroscope to identify chemical elements by the characteristic spectrum of radiation they emit when heated.*

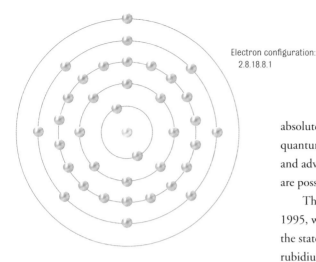

Electron configuration:
2.8.18.8.1

New horizons

Some might say that rubidium is currently underutilised in any meaningful applications, but that could change in the future. Rubidium gas has been used in the formation of a relatively new state of matter called a Bose–Einstein condensate (BEC). In BECs, gaseous atoms are condensed to produce particles that are held at temperatures just slightly above absolute zero (0 K). In this state, many quantum phenomena become apparent, and advanced studies at the atomic level are possible.

The first ever BEC was produced in 1995, when researchers in Colorado achieved the state by taking approximately 2,000 rubidium-87 atoms and cooling them to 170 nanokelvin, i.e., 0.000000170 K. Soon after, another group at MIT (Massachusetts Institute of Technology) used atoms of fellow group 1 element sodium to make a different BEC. The work of the two groups led to the award of the Nobel Prize in Physics in 2001. Since that time, lithium atoms have also been used to make BECs, but their real-world application remains a futuristic endeavour.

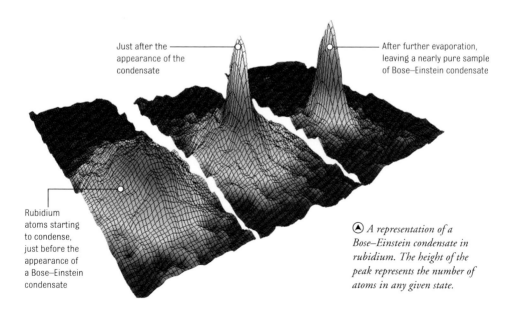

Just after the appearance of the condensate

After further evaporation, leaving a nearly pure sample of Bose–Einstein condensate

Rubidium atoms starting to condense, just before the appearance of a Bose–Einstein condensate

⊙ *A representation of a Bose–Einstein condensate in rubidium. The height of the peak represents the number of atoms in any given state.*

Cs Caesium

Chemical symbol	Cs
Atomic number	55
Atomic mass	132.91
Boiling point	671 °C (1240 °F)
Melting point	28.5 °C (83.3 °F)

Caesium is the alkali metal that is most likely to exist as a liquid under ambient conditions. The silvery-gold, soft metal melts at 28.4 °C (83 °F), just a few degrees above room temperature. Caesium has an elevated ability to lose its negative outer electron in chemical reactions, since the electron is held further from the positive nucleus than in any of the elements above it in group 1, and can thus be ripped away very easily.

Caesium was the first element found by Bunsen and Kirchhoff via their spectroscope method (see pp. 20–21). Using samples of mineral water as the source, the two chemists painstakingly removed known compounds from the water until they had concentrated liquor. Using the spectroscope that they had developed, they examined the light that was emitted when the water was exposed to a flame. They saw previously unobserved lines, and put this down to there being an undiscovered element present. The bright blue lines in caesium's emission spectrum inspired the element's name, since the Latin *caesius* means 'sky-blue'. The Latin influence persists in the IUPAC-recommended spelling of the element's name, caesium.

Atomic time

Caesium's spectral lines are linked to arguably its most important application: in atomic clocks. As with krypton and the metre (see pp. 212–13), the movement of electrons within atoms is such a reproducible event that it can be used as a standard by which SI (International System) units can be defined. In the case of caesium, it is the SI unit of time, the second, that is defined in terms of

◀ *Jack Parry (left) and Louis Essen (right) designed and built the world's first caesium atomic clock at the UK National Physical Laboratory in 1955.*

electron movement. The SI second is defined as: 'the duration of 9,192,631,770 periods of the radiation corresponding to the transition between the two, hyperfine levels of the ground state of the caesium-133 atom' (a caesium isotope). The transition of electrons from one place in the atom to another is associated with measurable periods of time. This electronic transition event in the caesium isotope is reliable enough to produce atomic clocks that are accurate to within one second every several million years.

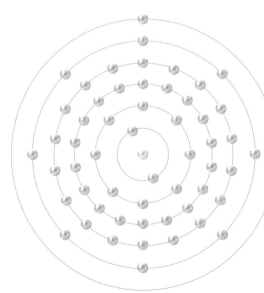

A view of the abandoned city of Pripyat in the Chernobyl exclusion zone. The nuclear disaster at Chernobyl in 1986 triggered the release of radioactive caesium-137 into the atmosphere.

Caesium-137

Another isotope of caesium has gained notoriety for its radioactive nature. Caesium-137 has been released into the atmosphere through weapons testing, and via the high-profile nuclear accidents in Chernobyl and Fukushima. Caesium-137 has several particularly nasty traits, ranging from its relatively long half-life of approximately thirty years – meaning that it stays present in the environment for a long time – and the solubility of salts that contain it – meaning that it can easily enter the water system and be spread liberally around the biosphere. As an alpha and gamma emitter, the isotope has the potential to be very harmful to human health, and the fact that, like thallium (pp. 110–11), it can mimic essential potassium in biological situations, makes it even more problematic.

Electron configuration:
2.8.18.18.8.1

Fr Francium

Chemical symbol	Fr
Atomic number	87
Atomic mass	223 (longest-living isotope)
Boiling point	677 °C (1251 °F)
Melting point	27 °C (81 °F)

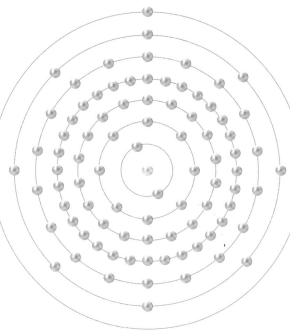

Electron configuration: 2.8.18.32.18.8.1

Since the reactivity of the alkali metals increases as one descends the group, it is not surprising that francium enjoys a somewhat mythical status as a highly dangerous element. In fact, there is really nothing to worry about. It is not that the predicted ire of francium is inaccurate, but simply that there is estimated to be only a few grams of francium in the earth's crust at any given moment.

False starts

Francium is another of the seven missing elements that were highlighted following Moseley's ordering of the periodic table via atomic number (p. 6). It is somewhat of a wonder that francium was ever discovered at all, given the scarcity of it, and the incredibly short half-lives exhibited by its isotopes. Francium was commonly known as eka-caesium at the outset of the search (appropriately, given its ultimate position in the periodic table), and over the years an unusually large number of false claims were made of its discovery. In the

As a result of Moseley's work on atomic numbers, seven 'missing' elements were discovered, including, in 1939, francium.

Atomic number	Element	Year of discovery
91	Protactinium	1917
72	Hafnium	1923
75	Rhenium	1925
43	Technetium	1937
87	Francium	1939
85	Astatine	1940

◀ *French physicist Marguerite Perey discovered francium in 1939 and named the element after her native country. Perey had been a student of Marie Curie.*

Eventually, in 1939, a French researcher solved the mystery of the missing element. Marguerite Perey (1909–1975), who had been an assistant to Marie Curie (1867–1934), was studying the radioactive nature of actinium, and noticed some unusual beta emission coming from her samples. She deduced that this radioactivity was not from the actinium itself, but that it was from another source. That source turned out to be the elusive francium.

Proving elusive

Chemical reactivity is one thing, but radioactivity is quite another. No stable isotopes of francium (an alarmingly radioactive element) exist on earth, and the ones that do occur (francium-223 and francium-221) are themselves products of other nuclear decay series. Each of these isotopes have half-lives that are just a matter of minutes, and as a result, their existence is only fleeting. That is why virtually no francium exists on earth at any given moment.

While francium might have a few interesting stories associated with it, its scarcity and intensely radioactive nature mean that it is one of the few elements on the periodic table with basically no practical applications. Any studies of it have been isolated to research facilities, working with just a few hundred thousand atoms, and the element has never been observed as an isolated sample.

process it was given various bogus names. Fred Allison (1882–1974) made the most infamous of the false 'discoveries' when he was a professor at what is now Auburn University, in Alabama, USA (formerly Alabama Polytechnic Institute) in the late 1920s. Allison claimed to have discovered both element number 87 and element number 85 via what he called magneto-optic spectroscopy, or the 'Allison Effect'. Unfortunately, despite multiple claims of various new discoveries – including Allison's naming element 87 virginium after his native state of Virginia – Allison's theories and claims were ultimately debunked and are now often cited as classic examples of pathological science.

◀ *Mendeleev predicted the existence of ten new elements, of which seven were eventually discovered.*

Alkaline earth metals

The group 2 elements share many similarities with their group 1 neighbours to the left, inasmuch as they are not found free in nature and are reactive, but each of the extreme properties found in group 1 is toned down a little for group 2. A little harder, a little more dense, and a little less reactive than the alkali metals, the alkaline earth metals also have higher melting and boiling points. Compared to metals not in group 1, however, the alkaline earths are fairly soft and quite reactive.

On the following pages:

Be **Beryllium**   **Sr** **Strontium**

Mg **Magnesium**   **Ba** **Barium**

Ca **Calcium**   **Ra** **Radium**

1 H																	2 He
3 Li	4 Be											5 B	6 C	7 N	8 O	9 F	10 Ne
11 Na	12 Mg											13 Al	14 Si	15 P	16 S	17 Cl	18 Ar
19 K	20 Ca	21 Sc	22 Ti	23 V	24 Cr	25 Mn	26 Fe	27 Co	28 Ni	29 Cu	30 Zn	31 Ga	32 Ge	33 As	34 Se	35 Br	36 Kr
37 Rb	38 Sr	39 Y	40 Zr	41 Nb	42 Mo	43 Tc	44 Ru	45 Rh	46 Pd	47 Ag	48 Cd	49 In	50 Sn	51 Sb	52 Te	53 I	54 Xe
55 Cs	56 Ba	57–71	72 Hf	73 Ta	74 W	75 Re	76 Os	77 Ir	78 Pt	79 Au	80 Hg	81 Tl	82 Pb	83 Bi	84 Po	85 At	86 Rn
87 Fr	88 Ra	89–103	104 Rf	105 Db	106 Sg	107 Bh	108 Hs	109 Mt	110 Ds	111 Rg	112 Cn	113 Nh	114 Fl	115 Mc	116 Lv	117 Ts	118 Og

57 La	58 Ce	59 Pr	60 Nd	61 Pm	62 Sm	63 Eu	64 Gd	65 Tb	66 Dy	67 Ho	68 Er	69 Tm	70 Yb	71 Lu
89 Ac	90 Th	91 Pa	92 U	93 Np	94 Pu	95 Am	96 Cm	97 Bk	98 Cf	99 Es	100 Fm	101 Md	102 No	103 Lr

The earths

The collective name for the members of group 2 derives from the historic naming of the oxides of these elements. They were first given the name 'earths', and there was much conjecture as to whether what ultimately turned out to be oxides were indeed elements at all. Even when it was established that the oxides were in fact compounds that could yield the group 2 elements, the original name stuck, and beryllium, magnesium, calcium, strontium, barium and radium became the alkaline earths. As with group 1, the alkali/alkaline part of the name comes from the fact that the oxides and hydroxides of the group 1 and group 2 elements are chemical bases, and the fact that an alkali is a base.

Ⓐ *Salts of the alkaline earth metals strontium, calcium, and barium are used in fireworks in order to produce vivid colours.*

Health and wellness

Magnesium and calcium are both essential elements to humans and other life forms. As the metal at the centre of chlorophyll – the green pigment that allows plants to convert light to energy – magnesium is vital; as a crucial component of bones and teeth, calcium is central to skeletal health. Radium, on the other hand, is a ferociously radioactive element that has done much damage to health over the years. Magnesium is a dangerously flammable element (unusual for a metal) that burns with a tremendously bright, white light, and that property has been harnessed in both commercial and military applications. The salts of strontium, calcium and barium are used in fireworks, since they provide stunning colours when heated.

Be Beryllium

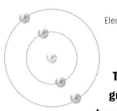

Chemical symbol	Be
Atomic number	4
Atomic mass	9.0122
Boiling point	2468 °C (4474 °F)
Melting point	1287 °C (2349 °F)

Electron configuration: 2.2

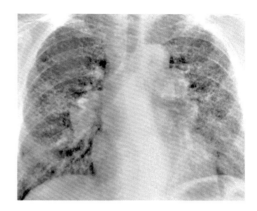

Ⓐ *The occupational disease berylliosis is a chronic lung condition that is caused by exposure to beryllium and its compounds.*

The lightest of the group 2 elements, beryllium gets its name from the mineral beryl. For over 150 years element number 4 was named glucinium from 'glucina', the word used to describe the oxide (or earth) of beryllium. That word in turn is derived from the Greek *glukus,* meaning 'sweet'. Apparently, beryllium compounds are sweet to the taste.

Ⓥ *Aquamarine is a precious variety of beryl, a mineral ore of beryllium.*

Tasting used as a method of chemical analysis is pretty ill-advised under the best of circumstances, but applying this dubious 'technique' to beryllium is even more foolhardy, as we will see. As a toxic and radioactive element, beryllium is pretty nasty stuff. Long-term exposure to the element and its compounds can lead to the debilitating lung disease berylliosis. The disease, which causes a wide variety of symptoms, including shortness of breath, coughing and chest pain, is occupational in nature, meaning that it is usually only contracted by those exposed to beryllium via their working conditions. One particularly vulnerable group were workers employed in the fluorescent light industry, which used beryllium until the practice was discontinued in 1949. In addition to berylliosis, exposure to beryllium can cause long-term poisoning and skin problems. Throw in the fact that beryllium and its compounds are known carcinogens, and you've got quite the mix! On the flip side, beryllium is certainly an attractive element. Both in its steely-grey metallic form and in the brilliant blues and greens of the aquamarine and emerald gemstones that contain the oxide, element number 4 has its moments – one just needs to choose them carefully.

Toxic bulbs

Like another, better-known element, lead (see pp. 112–13), beryllium's uses over the years have evolved considerably because its toxic nature became apparent long after it had been deployed in many places. Until the late 1940s, for example, the element was used in the manufacture of fluorescent lightbulbs. The process caused problems for the workers, but the disposal of spent lamps produced a potential problem for consumers too. As beryllium's toxic nature became apparent, the use of beryllium compounds was phased out.

Neutron discovery

In a much more positive contribution to chemistry, beryllium was at the heart of the discovery of the neutron in 1932. As part of the process that James Chadwick used in his experiments that led to the discovery of the neutral subatomic particle, a beryllium nucleus was bombarded with alpha particles, and a carbon atom and a neutron were the result:

$$^{9}_{4}Be + ^{4}_{2}He \rightarrow ^{12}_{6}C + ^{1}_{0}n$$

In more modern chemistry, beryllium has a couple of important applications. With copper, in an alloy containing only about 2 percent beryllium, it produces a much harder, more resilient version of pure copper, while maintaining the excellent conductivity of the heavier metal. In a more sinister role, it is used in the manufacture of nuclear weaponry, where its light but strong nature is put to use in the so-called 'pit' of nuclear weapons. The beryllium is used to encase the fissile material where it acts as a neutron reflector, trapping the neutrons that cause the chain reaction. In turn, the element also acts as a tamper, momentarily containing the initial chain reaction, making its ultimate release even more devastating.

⊙ *James Chadwick (left) with General Leslie R. Groves, Jr., the director of the Manhattan Project. Chadwick discovered the neutron by bombarding a beryllium nucleus with alpha particles.*

Mg Magnesium

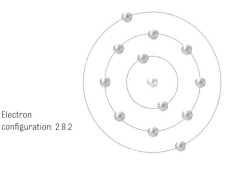

Electron
configuration: 2.8.2

Chemical symbol	Mg
Atomic number	12
Atomic mass	24.305
Boiling point	1090 °C (1994 °F)
Melting point	650 °C (1202 °F)

KEY FIGURE

JOSEPH
BLACK

1728–1799

Scottish chemist and physician Joseph Black 'discovered' magnesium by distinguishing between magnesia and lime (the oxides of magnesium and calcium, respectively). However, this accomplishment was only one of Black's chemical triumphs. He identified carbon dioxide (known as 'fixed air' at the time) as a unique gas and investigated its properties, and he pioneered work on latent heat of fusion, latent heat of vaporization and specific heat capacity – all important concepts in physical chemistry.

As an important structural metal, and via its use in alloys, element number 12 combines strength with a relatively low density to make it an attractive metal where such a combination is desirable – in the aerospace industry, for example. Discovered in 1755 by the Scottish chemist Joseph Black, it was another of the elements isolated via electrolysis by Humphry Davy in 1808.

In its silvery-grey metallic form, magnesium is highly reactive. It is also extremely flammable when in its powder or other finely divided form. Perhaps the most infamous magnesium fire of all time occurred during the 1955 Le Mans 24-hour race, when a car crashed into the crowd, killing its driver, Pierre Levegh, and 83 spectators. The devastation caused was exacerbated by the fire that resulted from the crash, and the fact that the car's bodywork had a high magnesium content was blamed. Rescue workers, unaware of the chemical reaction that would be caused, attempted to extinguish the fire with water. The magnesium reacted with steam to release flammable hydrogen gas, and as a result the fire was greatly intensified.

⊙ *Chlorophyll is at the centre of the chemistry of all green plants, and at the centre of every chlorophyll molecule, is a magnesium ion.*

Magnesium's potentially hazardous nature is contradicted by its absolutely essential role in animal and plant life. As a component of a number of enzyme-based reactions in animals, it helps to regulate energy transfer, muscle action, and a host of other biological functions. The metal also sits at the centre of the chlorophyll molecule that plants use in photosynthesis when they convert light to energy.

Sacrificial protection

Like zinc, magnesium's reactivity can be put to use in the role of a sacrificial metal. Just like element number 30, magnesium's propensity to release electrons more readily than other metals means that it can protect those other metals from corrosion. In almost every example of the alloying of magnesium, the strength-to-weight advantages of the group 2 element are exploited. With aluminium, it produces the alloys magnox and magnalium. Magnalium offers enhanced strength without the addition of mass, and is used in aircraft and automobile manufacture, as well as in expensive lightweight bicycle frames.

Perilous production

Magnesium is not a cheap metal when compared to many others, not least of all because a lot of it is produced via electrolysis, a process that uses electricity. The cost means that recycling the metal is an important part of its life cycle, and magnesium recycling plants are common. With a large amount of magnesium concentrated in one place, those plants can pose a significant fire hazard, and in two separate incidents in Ohio, USA, in 2003 and 2012, massive infernos occurred at magnesium recycling plants. When controlled, the intense, bright white light that is emitted by burning small pieces of magnesium can be used in fireworks. Similarly, magnesium was a crucial component of the flash powder used in early flash photography. Lighting the explosive mixture of powdered magnesium and the strong oxidising agent potassium chlorate by hand, with a naked flame, often proved to be quite the adventure!

Ca Calcium

Chemical symbol	Ca
Atomic number	20
Atomic mass	40.078
Boiling point	1484 °C (2703 °F)
Melting point	842 °C (1548 °F)

Calcium is far more likely to be encountered in everyday life as one of its compounds than in its elemental state. As an element, it is a silvery metal like its fellows in group 2, but in most of its compounds it appears as a hard, white solid. Its most common forms on earth include gypsum, marble and lime – calcium sulfate, calcium carbonate and calcium oxide, respectively.

Lime was one of Antoine Lavoisier's (1743–94) original elements – more precisely, one of his 'earths'. It took until 1808, when Humphry Davy isolated calcium via electrolysis, before calcium's status as an element was proven. As a pure, metallic element, calcium's uses are somewhat limited, but in its various compounds it finds many uses.

Beyond the skeletal system

Most people think of calcium as being an essential element for health because of the compounds that it forms in teeth and bones, which strengthen the skeletal parts of most animals. Those people are correct, of course, but calcium is so much more than simply an element of structure in the body. It has a role in transmitting nerve signals via its ionic conductivity, and has an important job in

⊙ *Various calcium compounds can be found in many building materials, such as concrete.*

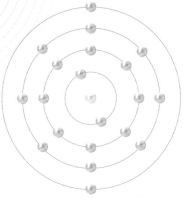

Electron configuration:
2.8.8.2

regulating the pH of blood. Outside the human body, compounds of calcium are used in agriculture to regulate acidity in soil. The chief compound used in that role is calcium hydroxide, $Ca(OH)_2$, also known as slaked lime. Slaked lime is derived from quicklime, calcium oxide, by the addition of water. It has been used as a building material (as a component of mortar) for thousands of years, and is still a hugely important chemical in the construction industry (as a component of cement) and in a host of other applications.

Hard water

Along with the element directly above it, magnesium, calcium imparts a property to water that huge resources are devoted to eradicating. The phenomenon, known simply as 'hard water', is caused by the presence of Ca^{2+} (and Mg^{2+}) ions. These ions have several problematic effects, including making it more difficult to form lathers with soaps because of the formation of insoluble stearates, or soap 'scums', and the buildup of 'limescale' on

Ⓐ *The familiar build-up of limescale in household electrical appliances that are exposed to hard water is caused by the presence of calcium ions.*

the components of water-heating elements such as those found in electric kettles. The hard, white deposits are essentially calcium carbonate that has been formed from the calcium ions present in the hard water. The buildup of such a solid can cause blockages of the system, and a significant reduction in the efficiency of the heating elements.

Sr Strontium

Chemical symbol	Sr
Atomic number	38
Atomic mass	87.62
Boiling point	1377 °C (2510.60 °F)
Melting point	777 °C (1431 °F)

A close relative of calcium by virtue of its place on the periodic table, strontium also has a significant historical connection to the element above it, and indeed to element number 56 directly below it. As Humphry Davy continued to romp through the periodic table – isolating metals left, right and centre via electrolysis – strontium, like calcium and barium, was one of his conquests. He first isolated the metal in 1808.

Electron configuration:
2.8.18.8.2

In terms of chemistry, Scotland has a few claims to fame. Two of the most obvious reside among the alkaline earth metals of group 2. Along with Scotsman Joseph Black, who is credited with the discovery of magnesium, Scotland also yielded strontium, from a mineral first found in the small mining village of Strontian in the West Highlands. A Scottish doctor by the name of Adair Crawford (1748–1795) noticed that the mineral, which was initially thought to be a barium compound but ultimately turned out to be strontium carbonate, was distinct from similar barium minerals in terms of its properties. Thus, element number 38 was born.

A sinister isotope

In keeping with the other group 2 elements, strontium is another soft, silvery, reactive metal that will quickly form an oxide layer on its surface. It exists as a number of non-radioactive isotopes in nature, but in an analogous situation to cobalt, it has one isotope whose reputation has gone before it: strontium-90. Strontium-90 can pose a serious threat to human health. The insidious nature of the isotope lies in its ability to mimic calcium, and thus find its way into bones. Once inside, strontium-90 can do untold damage to the bone, the bone marrow and the surrounding tissue. Strontium-90 is not a naturally occurring isotope of element number 38, so where does it come from? Like cobalt-60 (see pp. 54–55), strontium-90 is a product of nuclear reactions, specifically from the fallout from nuclear testing that took place in the late 1940s and early 1960s in the United States and

The 'Baker' explosion, part of Operation Crossroads, a nuclear weapon test carried out by the US military at Bikini Atoll, Marshall Islands, in 1946.

the Marshall Islands in the Pacific. This testing caused the distribution of strontium-90 over a wide area, and the isotope subsequently made its way into the food chain via plants and animals. In 1959 the Greater St. Louis Citizens' Committee for Nuclear Information initiated the collection of hundreds of thousands of children's baby teeth, and it was quickly established that there had been a significant accumulation of strontium-90 in the children. The outcry surrounding the discovery led to a ban on above-ground nuclear testing. In more recent events, the nuclear accidents at Chernobyl in Ukraine in 1986 and Fukushima in Japan in 2011 have also had the effect of distributing stronoium-90 into the environment.

Filling holes

In happier and more benign uses, strontium's ability to impart a bright crimson colour to a flame is taken advantage of in fireworks and emergency flares. In the manufacture of toothpaste made for sensitive teeth, strontium acetate, $Sr(CH_3COO)_2$, and strontium chloride, $SrCl_2$, utilise the fact that strontium can act like calcium, to help fill the microscopic holes in teeth.

Many children donated baby teeth to the Greater St. Louis Citizens' Committee for Nuclear Information study into the effects of radioactive strontium-90 on bones.

Ba Barium

Chemical symbol	Ba
Atomic number	56
Atomic mass	137.33
Boiling point	1845 °C (3353 °F)
Melting point	727 °C (1341 °F)

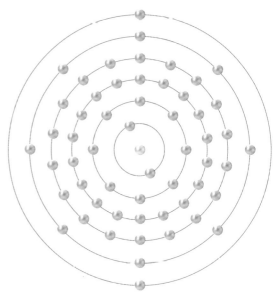

Electron configuration:
2.8.18.18.8.2

Barium's name is derived from the Greek *barys*, meaning 'heavy', but that moniker is falsely applied to the element itself. In fact, barium is a relatively light element, with literally scores of others having higher densities. Where the heaviness *is* manifest is in the compounds of barium. Sitting towards the bottom of group 2, barium is a highly reactive element, and as such is not found free in nature.

One of the most important of those compounds is barium sulfate, $BaSO_4$. Barium sulfate is found in nature as the mineral barite, and is a tremendously dense substance. It finds two major applications where its sheer mass and compactness are put to contrasting uses. In oil drilling, barium sulfate is added to the 'mud' that is used around the well and drill bit in order to help them withstand the tremendous pressures that are created at such depths. In this role it is often referred to as a literal 'weighting agent'. The second application is a little more delicate, but nevertheless equally important.

◄ The common mineral barite, also known as 'desert rose', is a source of barium. Other minerals that contain barium include benitoite and witherite.

Barium X-rays

Most of the tissue that makes up the human gut will allow X-rays to pass straight through, so it is not possible to use the rays as a diagnostic tool for the digestive system in the way that they can be used to image human bones. In steps barium sulfate, in the form of the ominous-sounding 'barium enema'. Barium sulfate can either be swallowed (a barium swallow), or alternatively inserted into the gut via the anus. Both methods fill the gastrointestinal tract with the impenetrable barium salt, and if exposed to X-rays, it will produce useful images for medical diagnostics. Barium's function in this particular compound and this application is in stark (and ironic) contrast to a number of its other, more soluble salts. As salts such as chloride, bromide, and iodide, barium is a dangerously toxic element that can cause vomiting, diarrhoea and other digestive ailments. If one is going to ingest barium, it's pretty important to get the right compound!

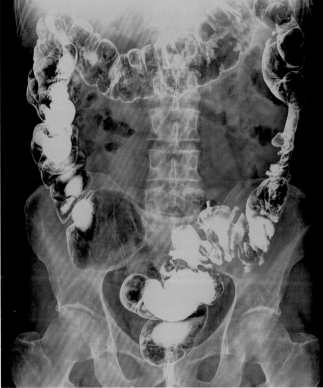

Ⓐ So-called 'barium meals' are given to patients as a diagnostic tool to allow investigation of the stomach and small bowel with X-rays.

Compounds made in situ

Like strontium, barium's ability to impart pleasing colours to flames is used in the manufacture of fireworks, and the compound most often used is barium chloride. However, it's not quite as simple as that. Barium chloride is hygroscopic, meaning that it easily absorbs water from the atmosphere. Of course, this makes the compound 'wet', which creates a serious problem when one is attempting to set fire to fireworks. The ingenious solution involves introducing other compounds of barium and chlorine into the firework, and allowing the formation of barium chloride in the gaseous phase that forms once the firework is lit. In that way, the fireworks can be easily ignited and the characteristic green colour of barium salts can light up the night sky.

Ra Radium

Chemical symbol	Ra
Atomic number	88
Atomic mass	226 (longest-living isotope)
Boiling point	1737 °C (3159 °F)
Melting point	700 °C (1292 °F)

One of the more famous elements – at least in terms of its history – radium was discovered and named by Marie Curie (1867–1934) and her husband, Pierre (1859–1906), in Paris in 1898. Inextricably linked with radioactivity, and not only via its name, radium has a truly extraordinary history of bizarre use in 'medicine', being represented at one time or another as a cure-all for many ailments and conditions including, ironically, cancer.

⊙ Marie and Pierre Curie discovered radium in 1898 during their pioneering work on radioactvity. They named the new element after the Latin word for 'ray'.

Like caesium and strontium before, radium was identified via the unique spectrum that it produced on spectroscopic analysis. It was named for the blue glowing rays of light that the element produces in air, and it is this property that was put to use in one of radium's most notorious applications.

Radium dials

The Radium Luminous Material Corporation used radium, in combination with other chemicals, in its luminous paints. In the early part of the twentieth century, these paints were used to produce clock, watch and dial faces that would glow in the dark. One technique commonly used by the young women employed to apply the paint was to bring the paintbrushes to a fine point by licking them. The prolonged and intense exposure to the radioactive radium in the paint caused terrible radiation sickness, cancers and many deaths among the workers. The fact that the owners of the company knew about the risks but attempted to cover up the dangers led to a huge controversy and court proceedings, with the company eventually settling with the women. However, that was not before the devastating effects of radium poisoning had gripped the lives of so many. There have been a number of pop-culture references to the story, including, in 2016, Kate Moore's book *The Radium Girls*.

The Revigator

The controlled and more studious use of radium as a treatment for cancer makes it an important element in twenty-first century medicine, but one hundred years earlier, soon after its discovery, it was used in an almost completely indiscriminate manner. Touted by many as a tonic for general good health, it was marketed as a cure for a large number of ailments via the 'Radium Ore Revigator'. The Revigator was a ceramic container that was coated on the inside with a whole host of dubious chemicals, among them a uranium ore called carnotite. Traces of radium were present in the ore, and the idea was that water would be stored in the device overnight, and that the resultant radioactive concoction would invigorate the water and promise good health! The advertising told potential customers that the water would be infused with 'the lost element of original freshness – radioactivity'. In the 1920s and '30s, several hundreds of thousands of these devices were sold before the hazards associated with them were finally brought to light. In a later analysis, it was determined that the arsenic and lead that were also present in the jars were likely to be equally to blame for the sickness that the 'medical' device inflicted.

Ⓐ *The 'radium girls' working in a watch factory. The young women contracted radiation poisoning from painting dials with self-luminous paint containing radium.*

Electron configuration:
2.8.18.32.18.8.2

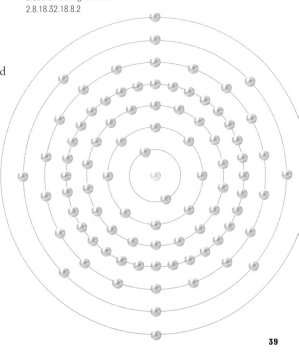

Transition metals

The elements in groups 3 to 12 are collectively known as the transition metals. English chemist Charles R. Bury (1890–1968) coined the name in 1921, when he referred to the sequence of metals starting at titanium and passing through to copper as a *transition series*. He was describing the 'transition' from eight electrons in the third electron layer to a saturated layer of 18.

On the following pages:

Sc	Scandium	Ru	Ruthenium
Ti	Titanium	Rh	Rhodium
V	Vanadium	Pd	Palladium
Cr	Chromium	Ag	Silver
Mn	Manganese	Cd	Cadmium
Fe	Iron	Hf	Hafnium
Co	Cobalt	Ta	Tantalum
Ni	Nickel	W	Tungsten
Cu	Copper	Re	Rhenium
Zn	Zinc	Os	Osmium
Y	Yttrium	Ir	Iridium
Zr	Zirconium	Pt	Platinum
Nb	Niobium	Au	Gold
Mo	Molybdenum	Hg	Mercury
Tc	Technetium		

1 H																	2 He
3 Li	4 Be											5 B	6 C	7 N	8 O	9 F	10 Ne
11 Na	12 Mg											13 Al	14 Si	15 P	16 S	17 Cl	18 Ar
19 K	20 Ca	21 Sc	22 Ti	23 V	24 Cr	25 Mn	26 Fe	27 Co	28 Ni	29 Cu	30 Zn	31 Ga	32 Ge	33 As	34 Se	35 Br	36 Kr
37 Rb	38 Sr	39 Y	40 Zr	41 Nb	42 Mo	43 Tc	44 Ru	45 Rh	46 Pd	47 Ag	48 Cd	49 In	50 Sn	51 Sb	52 Te	53 I	54 Xe
55 Cs	56 Ba	57–71	72 Hf	73 Ta	74 W	75 Re	76 Os	77 Ir	78 Pt	79 Au	80 Hg	81 Tl	82 Pb	83 Bi	84 Po	85 At	86 Rn
87 Fr	88 Ra	89–103	104 Rf	105 Db	106 Sg	107 Bh	108 Hs	109 Mt	110 Ds	111 Rg	112 Cn	113 Nh	114 Fl	115 Mc	116 Lv	117 Ts	118 Og

57 La	58 Ce	59 Pr	60 Nd	61 Pm	62 Sm	63 Eu	64 Gd	65 Tb	66 Dy	67 Ho	68 Er	69 Tm	70 Yb	71 Lu
89 Ac	90 Th	91 Pa	92 U	93 Np	94 Pu	95 Am	96 Cm	97 Bk	98 Cf	99 Es	100 Fm	101 Md	102 No	103 Lr

Classification confusion

You may think that we are simply talking about elements 21–30 in the third period, 39–48 in the fourth period, 72–80 in the fifth period and 104–112 in the sixth, but of course, as we see with other attempts to classify the elements in some gross manner, it is never quite that simple. To make matters even more complicated, that same section of the periodic table also goes by another name, the 'd-block', which refers to the fact that within that section, d-orbitals are being filled.

Even more confusingly, some classifications of the transition metals will include the actinoids and lanthanoids, and there is debate as to the role of other metals in this collection. For example, one definition of transition metals says that they are elements that exhibit partially filled d-subshells in their ions. This presents a problem for elements such as scandium and zinc that commonly form ions where the d-subshells are completely empty and entirely filled, respectively. So, as with our other 'forced' groupings, we need to apply a little latitude rather than fulfilling a rigid requirement.

Chemical characteristics

So what commonalities can we safely apply to the transition metals that are chosen here? In the simplest terms, these are the elements in the fourth, fifth and sixth periods whose final electron enters the 3d, 4d or 5d sublevel. The similarities in the electronic configurations of these malleable, high-melting-point lustrous metals lend them a few characteristic properties. Such properties include their

⊛ One highly visible characteristic of transition metals is their ability to form a wide variety of brightly coloured salts.

ability to exhibit multiple oxidation states (cf. group 1, pp. 12–25, and group 2 metals, pp. 26–39), their inclination to form complex ions, and their use as catalysts. As complex ions such as $[Cu(H_2O)_6]^{2+}$ (blue) and $[CuCl_4]^{2-}$ (yellow), transition metals bring colour to aqueous solutions. If you have ever seen a stereotypical chemistry lab depicted on television with exotic glassware filled with brightly coloured liquids, then there's a good chance that some transition metals were involved. As catalysts, the metals and their compounds have important roles in industrial applications and chemical manufacture. One such example is in the making of margarine, where nickel is commonly used as a catalyst.

Ultimately, however one classifies the transition metal/d-block elements, there is a ton of great chemistry in there!

Sc Scandium

Chemical symbol	Sc
Atomic number	21
Atomic mass	44.956
Boiling point	2836 °C (5136 °F)
Melting point	1541 °C (2806 °F)

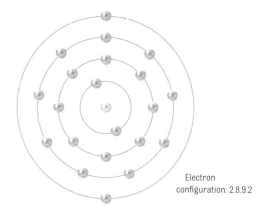

Electron configuration: 2.8.9.2

Whether used in guns or in high-performance jet fighters, scandium is an element with a reputation for being a delicate influencer. A soft, silver-coloured metal, it is often alloyed with other metals to subtly change their properties, and in the process, to make those other metals more useful. Mendeleev predicted scandium's existence long before it was actually discovered.

⊙ Elemental scandium, with its silvery, grey colour, is a typical metal. It is found in many naturally occurring minerals such as scandiobabingtonite.

S candium gets its name from the Latin for Scandinavia, *Scandia*, where Lars Fredrik Nilson (1840–1899) first discovered it in 1879. Mendeleev had left a gap in his periodic table for an element that would have an atomic mass of approximately 45, and that he called eka-boron. It turned out that scandium matched the predicted properties of eka-boron very closely, and thus another of the Russian's predicted elements had been found. Like some of his other predictions (but not all), Mendeleev's guess was astonishingly close to the truth.

High-performance alloys

Scandium is not only found in Scandinavia these days; in fact, it is found in many ores in a number of places on earth, but none of the sources are particularly plentiful. As a result, scandium is not cheap. That's a shame, because it means that scandium tends to find few widespread commercial applications. However, one important use of the metal is in an alloy that it makes with aluminium. Even very small amounts of scandium (less than 1 percent) can dramatically increase the hardness of the lightweight metal, making it suitable in

applications where pure aluminium might not be viable. This scandium–aluminium alloy has been used extensively in constructing fighter aircraft (especially by the Russians), and has found use in high-performance sports equipment such as racing bicycle frames and baseball bats. The US gun maker Smith & Wesson produces a range of guns that it labels 'Sc/S', for 'scandium/stainless steel', as the collection of weapons uses a scandium alloy to form part of the gun.

Triple charge

Much of scandium's chemistry revolves around the +3 oxidation state it achieves when it loses its 4s and 3d electrons. Mendeleev had originally thought that scandium would be similar to boron, and the fact that element number 21 forms ions with the same charge as those of group 13 proves that he was right. In that +3 state, scandium forms a compound with iodine, ScI_3, which has an important application. Since the late 1960s, scandium(III)

Scandium's role as a high-performance metal is exemplified by its use in modern jet-fighter aircraft.

iodide has been used to create high-intensity lightbulbs that have an interesting property: they mimic natural sunlight very well. This makes them useful in applications such as television and photography, where natural light generally produces better results.

Scandium exists on earth as only one isotope, scandium-45, but a synthetic radioactive isotope, scandium-46, has found use as a tracer. By introducing radioactive atoms into a system where fluids move through pipes, the flow can be monitored. This has been utilised in the oil industry, where leaking pipes can be identified by the detection of the radioactive isotope. Although subject to regulation, if isotopes with relatively short half-lives of less than 120 days are used (scandium-46 has a half-life of approximately 84 days), then any risk to health or the environment is minimised.

Ti Titanium

Chemical symbol	Ti
Atomic number	22
Atomic mass	47.867
Boiling point	3287 °C (5949 °F)
Melting point	1668 °C (3034 °F)

Titanium is synonymous with toughness. That reputation is well earned and not without reason, since element number 22 is a material with one of the highest strength-to-weight ratios among the transition metals. The element's strength is, of course, the source of its name, since the metal was christened after the Greek gods known as the Titans, who were revered for their incredible strength.

Strong and light

As a metal with high strength and relative lightness, titanium is immensely useful, whether in its pure metal form or in alloys. Many parts of jet engines are constructed from titanium and its alloys, and not only for the strength-to-weight advantages: Titanium is also incredibly resistant to corrosion. This combination of properties makes for an attractive material. Alloys that combine titanium with another light but strong metal, aluminium, are common, and include the prosaically named Ti-3Al-8V-6Cr-4Mo-4Zr. Also known as Titanium Beta C, the alloy's former designation gives the percentages of aluminium, vanadium, chromium, molybdenum and zirconium that are alloyed with titanium to produce a particularly strong and corrosion-resistant material, which is, once again, used in various aircraft parts.

The metal is also sometimes used in the manufacture of golf clubs. The combination of a light weight and strength is certainly advantageous, but the intense marketing surrounding the idea that 'titanium can improve your game' seems at best optimistic. What is known is that if such a club strikes a rock in the rough, then sparks with temperatures of over 1,650 °C (3,000 °F) can result, and such incidents have allegedly caused a number of brush fires on golf courses.

◀ *Resistance to corrosion is seldom more important than in jet engines. As such, titanium plays a vital role in many aircraft components.*

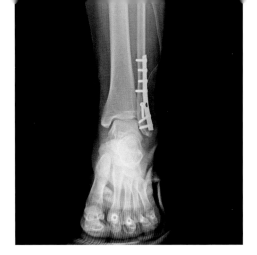

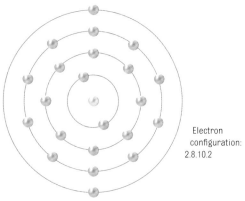

Many people have had bones repaired with titanium plates and screws. The element's corrosion resistance and high strength make it a good choice for surgical repairs.

Electron configuration: 2.8.10.2

Titanium body parts

Titanium is highly resistant to corrosion because, like aluminium, it rapidly forms an oxide layer on the surface that protects the pure metal underneath from attack. Its ability to resist oxidation means that it is a metal with important medical applications, as it can be implanted in various ways inside the body. Since it is used to produce replacement hip joints, and the screws and plates used to repair badly broken bones, there are a lot of people walking around with titanium inside them – it might just be the element that is responsible for the most alarms sounded by metal detectors at airports across the world!

Titanium dioxide white

The titanium dioxide that is formed on the surface of the metal is incredibly important in preventing corrosion, but it is equally important as a compound in its own right. In the form of finely divided powder, TiO_2 has an extraordinary ability to coat and cover surfaces and to reflect light. It is a bright white pigment, and the combination of its coating and optical properties means that it is used extensively in paints, paper and plastics to give an opaque product. Titanium's popularity grew out of the need to find a replacement for white lead ($2PbCO_3 \cdot Pb(OH)_2$), a compound with similar properties that had been used in paints for centuries until the early part of the twentieth century. As lead's toxicity (see pp. 112–13) was becoming increasingly well understood, so alternatives were required.

High performance, lightweight sports equipment, such as these golf clubs, routinely contains titanium.

V Vanadium

Chemical symbol	V
Atomic number	23
Atomic mass	50.942
Boiling point	3407 °C (6165 °F)
Melting point	1910 °C (3470 °F)

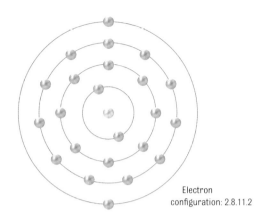

Electron
configuration: 2.8.11.2

Vanadium is a quintessential example of a transition metal, exhibiting many typical properties: the ability to form multiple oxidation states (charges), its use in catalysts, and its ability to exhibit many different colours in its various compounds. As vanadium passes through its oxidation states, spectacular colour changes can be observed, from purple, to green to blue, and finally to yellow.

④ *Vanadium is renowned for its multicoloured oxidation states, seen here, from left to right, in the +5, +4, +3, and +2 states.*

Kodachrome history

Like many other elements, vanadium has gone by a variety of names throughout its history, several of which related to the vivid colours of its compounds. One example is erythronium, derived from the Greek word for red, *erythros*. To paraphrase the great Paul Simon (b. 1941) in his famous 1973 song 'Kodachrome', when you think back on everything you learned in chemistry class in high school, perhaps one thing you may remember is the incredible array of wildly coloured compounds that vanadium can make. As such, it is appropriate that the story of vanadium's discovery is somewhat colourful.

Vanadium was 'discovered' twice – first by Andrés Manuel del Río (1764–1849) in 1801, only for him to be convinced that he hadn't actually found a new element, but simply encountered the already known (and equally colourful) chromium. In 1830, Swedish chemist Nils Sefström (1787–1845) 'rediscovered' vanadium in some iron compounds and named it after the Norse goddess *Vanadis*, who was renowned for her beauty.

Essential to humans and alloys

Vanadium played a central role in the development of the mass production of automobiles. Ford's Model T pioneered such production, and a pivotal part of its success was centered on vanadium. In the first decade of the twentieth century, vanadium steel was made exclusively in Europe, but Henry Ford recognised that the increased strength, durability, and relatively lightweight nature of steels that included vanadium would be a huge asset to the production of his vehicles. He incorporated the new steels into many of his cars, and thus vanadium helped to successfully launch a whole industry. Very small amounts of the transition metal (sometimes less than 1 percent) can be introduced into steel to produce a dramatically harder product known as V-steel. It is also found in the logically, if unimaginatively, named Ti-6Al-4V, an alloy of titanium that contains 6 percent aluminium and 4 percent vanadium.

◉ *Henry Ford and his famous Model T motor car, which championed the use of steels containing vanadium, and helped to bring the element to prominence in the field of engineering.*

◉ *In V-steel, the hardness and durability of the ubiquitous alloy is enhanced by the addition of vanadium.*

Regarded as one of the essential elements (those crucial to life), even though it is only present in tiny amounts, vanadium's specific role in the body is subject to debate. Most research into its function has been carried out on animals, and human trials have had mixed results. For example, some studies suggest that vanadium may help to control blood sugar levels and improve insulin sensitivity in patients with diabetes, while others have contradicted those findings. Vanadium's most common oxide, V_2O_5, is a catalyst in the manufacture of the vital chemical sulfuric acid, which is used in the manufacture of hundreds of other important chemicals, such as fertilisers, paints, other acids and synthetic fibres.

Cr Chromium

Chemical symbol	Cr
Atomic number	24
Atomic mass	51.996
Boiling point	2671 °C (4840 °F)
Melting point	1907 °C (3465 °F)

Chromium's very name, taken from the Greek *chroma*, meaning 'colour', suggests a rich palette of hues. Indeed, element number 24 exhibits one of the quintessential properties of a transition metal: the ability to form coloured compounds. Chromium(III) oxide, Cr_2O_3, is one such compound, one that is used as a vibrant, bright-green pigment in paints, but it is as the equally attractive pure metal that chromium shines – quite literally.

Classic chrome

The familiar 'chrome' that one might see on classic cars or motorcycles is in fact a thin layer of pure chromium that is electroplated on top of another metal, often its transition metal companion, nickel. The chrome finish was designed to be both decorative and durable, but with the advent of cheaper, equally durable composite and plastic materials, the use of chromium in the automotive industry faded after its heyday in the 1950, '60s, and '70s.

Stainless

Chromium is the metal that makes stainless steel 'stainless'. The addition of various percentages of chromium to steel, usually in the range of approximately 10–30 percent, provides the alloy with a microscopic chromium oxide layer that does not diminish the lustrous appearance, but does afford it the ability to resist corrosion. Stainless steel is used in surgical instruments, cookware and kitchen utensils, and even in decorative construction, with New York City's Chrysler Building and St. Louis's Gateway Arch standing as two such examples.

Electron configuration:
2.8.13.1

◀ *Dark green chromium(III) oxide illustrates one quintessential property of the transition metals: their ability to produce brightly coloured compounds.*

⊙ *The aesthetic appeal of chromium metal has long been utilised, particularly in the motorcycle and motor car industry.*

Colourful past

Looking back to the colourful side of chromium's history, we find two other important pigments, the chromates of lead and barium. Known as lemon yellow and chrome yellow, respectively, these compounds have a somewhat checkered past in terms of their impact, both positive and negative. On the plus side of the ledger, the daughter of England's King George IV, Princess Charlotte of Wales (1796–1817), chose chrome yellow for the colour of one of her carriages, and this helped to promote the pigment as a fashionable one of the day. The downside of such popularization was that these pigments (and others) were also used as food colourings, especially in confectionery. Unfortunately, a combination of lead and chromium makes for a particularly poisonous concoction, and in 1854 the British medical journal *The Lancet* published an article under the heading 'POISONOUS COLOURED CONFECTIONERY'. The report cited an earlier 1830 article in the same journal that quoted a Dr. O'Shaughnessy as saying:

> In the following observations it is my principal aim to lay before the public and the medical profession a calm, dispassionate statement of the existence of various poisons (gamboge, lead, copper, mercury, and chromate of lead) in several articles of confectionery, the preparation of which, from their peculiar attractions to the younger branches of the community, has grown into a separate and most extensive branch of manufacture.

Needless to say, the practice was soon stopped.

Mn Manganese

Chemical symbol	Mn
Atomic number	25
Atomic mass	54.938
Boiling point	2061 °C (3742 °F)
Melting point	1246 °C (2275 °F)

Electron
configuration: 2.8.13.2

Manganese is found naturally in several minerals, often with its periodic table neighbour, iron. It is distinguished by the black colour of many of its naturally occurring compounds, especially in the historically important mineral pyrolusite, which is essentially manganese dioxide. Pyrolusite was used in glass and porcelain manufacture for adjusting colour, and as a black pigment, long before anyone realised that it contained an element.

Manganese metal was isolated in 1774, by the Swedish mineralogist Johan Gottlieb Gahn (1745–1818). Around that time, several chemists were experimenting with a number of manganese-containing compounds, but Gahn's pioneering work with a blowpipe (a device used to produce more efficient reduction by directing a steady stream of air into a Bunsen burner flame) on MnO_2 in the form of pyrolusite and carbon in the form of charcoal, produced the first pellets of the metal itself.

Symbolic and emblematic

Like some of its cousins among the transition metals, manganese is an essential element for humans. Most people have never come across manganese as a pure element – the metal is brittle and not particularly useful

◀ Manganese is a brittle and hard metal with a dark grey, silvery appearance. It occurs naturally in a number of minerals, including pyrolusite, which is essentially manganese dioxide.

unless used in alloys. However, like vanadium, manganese may be somewhat familiar to those who remember their school chemistry lessons. Schoolchildren sometimes encounter the substance as manganese(IV) oxide, a black, powdery compound that acts as a catalyst in the decomposition of hydrogen peroxide to produce oxygen and a compound the colour of blackcurrant juice: potassium manganate(VII), aka potassium permanganate. Manganese may seem somewhat familiar via its use as an oxidising agent in titrations, and via its antiseptic properties and use in water sterilisation.

Generations of the same schoolchildren have mixed up the symbols for magnesium (Mg) and manganese (Mn). The manifestation of element number 25 in distinctive compounds offers much scope for confusion.

▲ Megalodon *teeth found preserved in manganese compounds inspired the theory that a modern-day ancestor of the prehistoric shark lives on.*

A different kind of filling

Ask someone which metals they think were used in old-fashioned dental fillings, and they might mention mercury, tin, copper and silver. Although manganese is not on that list, there is a bizarre connection between teeth and manganese. In 1875, HMS *Challenger* was on a scientific mission around the world. During that expedition, the crew recovered an enormous number of teeth belonging to the huge prehistoric shark *Megalodon*. The teeth had been encrusted in compounds of manganese. The thickness of the manganese layers dated these teeth at millions of years old, but some others were found with much less Mn, which suggested that they were only a few thousand years old. This led to wild speculation that *Megalodon* might still be lurking in the most remote depths of the oceans today. Unfortunately for those hoping to encounter a monster 15-metre (50-foot) shark, however, there is no credible scientific evidence to back up this theory.

▼ *Potassium permanganate, also known as potassium manganate(VII), forms a distinctive purple colour in solution.*

Fe Iron

Chemical symbol	Fe
Atomic number	26
Atomic mass	55.845
Boiling point	2861 °C (5182 °F)
Melting point	1538 °C (2800 °F)

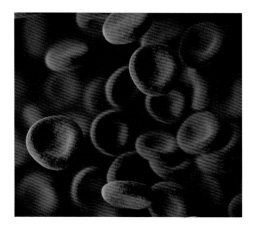

Used to create some of the earliest tools and implements, element number 26 has given its name to the period of history that started around 3,000–4,000 years ago: the Iron Age. The metal's utility has remained paramount even in modern times, especially in the ubiquitous alloy that it makes with carbon: steel.

⊙ *Iron pyrite, a common compound of iron and sulfur, has fooled many a gold prospector over the years.*

⊛ *The crucial iron-containing compound haemoglobin transports oxygen around the body, and gives red blood cells their characteristic red-pink colour.*

In the blood

Iron's role in construction is obvious, and often literally massive, but its role at the invisible, atomic level is even more important to humans. As an essential element, iron's most crucial function within the body is to regulate oxygen transport in the blood. At the centre of this crucial life-giving process is a protein called haemoglobin. This complex organic molecule has an iron(II) ion at its centre, and its role is to transport oxygen from the lungs to other parts of the body. Haemoglobin is found in the red blood cells of humans, and a deficiency of iron can lead to some serious medical issues. For centuries, iron tablets (now most usually in the form of iron(II) sulfate), have been given to patients with anaemic conditions. Anaemia has a number of symptoms – including fatigue – which manifest themselves when oxygen is inefficiently carried around the body.

Iron ores

Iron is the fourth most abundant element found in the earth's crust, but it is also quite abundant in the sun and stars. Partly due to its profusion, and partly due to its incredible usefulness, iron is likely to be the element that is the most mined on the planet. As ores, it appears as hematite (iron(III) oxide) as well as the mineral pyrite, FeS_2. Pyrite has the dubious distinction of being a mineral that has caused much consternation among prospectors the world over. Better known as 'fool's gold', its brassy yellow hue has raised the heart rate of many would-be gold hunters.

A magnetic element

Along with cobalt and nickel, iron is one of the magnetic elements. Since the term 'ferromagnetism' references iron itself, one might even consider it to be the quintessential one. Ferromagnetic materials align all of the much tinier magnetic fields created by their individual electrons into a consolidated group, thus creating a magnetic field strong enough to be experienced.

Electron configuration: 2.8.14.2

The red menace

Iron's usefulness in construction and industry comes with a cruel, chemical twist. In most of the environments that one might expect to find iron put to use, one also finds oxygen and water. The combination of those three substances means only one thing: rust. The sight of the oh-so-familiar reddish-brown compounds that corrode, and eventually destroy, iron objects by turning them into disintegrated, flaky masses is sometimes sad, and the process is one that humankind has been fighting for centuries. In his fascinating book *Rust: The Longest War* (2015), Jonathan Waldman catalogues the struggle that man has had with the hydrated iron oxide and hydroxide compounds that make up the red menace.

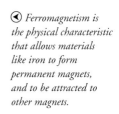
Ferromagnetism is the physical characteristic that allows materials like iron to form permanent magnets, and to be attracted to other magnets.

Co Cobalt

Chemical symbol	Co
Atomic number	27
Atomic mass	58.933
Boiling point	2927 °C (5301 °F)
Melting point	1495 °C (2723 °F)

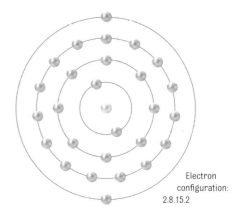

Electron
configuration:
2.8.15.2

As a shiny, silver-coloured, hard metal which is used extensively in alloys, and as a colouring agent in the familiar blue glass, cobalt seems somewhat unremarkable among its peers in the middle of the periodic table. That is largely true; however, one of its isotopes, cobalt-60, has projected a scary, if somewhat unfair reputation onto element number 27, as a potential constituent of a 'dirty' nuclear bomb.

Cobalt was discovered in a mineral found in some German mines in the 1730s by the chemist Georg Brandt (1694–1768). The name for element number 27 is derived from the mythical *Kobolds* (German for 'goblin' or 'gnome') that were thought to be mischievously preventing the mineral from yielding the copper that was thought to be present. In fact, there was no copper present in the ore in question, but rather it was mostly made up of cobalt arsenide, $CoAs_2$. Cobalt's association with the colour blue is due to its use as a pigment in painting, and in the manufacture of porcelain and glass. The chemical formula for the pigment known as cobalt blue is $CoAl_2O_4$.

◀ *Cobalt occurs naturally only in minerals and not as the free metal. When extracted, it has a silvery appearance.*

⊙ *For thousands of years cobalt has been used as a pigment for glass and ceramic glazes, where the element imparts a distinctive blue colour.*

'Dirty' bombs

There is only one naturally occurring isotope of cobalt, cobalt-59, and it is not radioactive. The nasty isotope is the synthetic cobalt-60. As a gamma ray emitter it has a relatively long half-life, and if left unchecked has a terrifying potential to unleash massive doses of lethal radiation across large areas. As such, cobalt-60 has been discussed as a potential component of a 'dirty' bomb, one where the impact of the initial blast is 'enhanced' by the lingering and widespread nuclear fallout, which would leave large areas of land uninhabitable for decades after the initial event. Cobalt-60 can cause cancer, but ironically, the power of cobalt-60, when harnessed properly, has been used to treat cancers, too.

Quebec's cobalt beer

The historical impact of cobalt on health has not been limited to its nuclear capacity, either. In the late 1960s, a bizarre tale emerged in Canada, where excessive beer-drinking became associated with heart conditions observed in a certain group of men. Several died, and the conundrum was not solved until a common thread was found: all of the men were drinking beer from one particular brewery. When it was discovered that the brewery was adding cobalt sulfate to its beer in order to increase its head retention, cobalt poisoning was diagnosed as the culprit. Known as Quebec beer-drinkers' cardiomyopathy, the condition and its causes were reported in the *Canadian Medical Association Journal* in 1967.

Ni Nickel

Chemical symbol	Ni
Atomic number	28
Atomic mass	58.693
Boiling point	2913 °C (5275 °F)
Melting point	1455 °C (2651 °F)

As one of the metals historically used to make coins, nickel has become synonymous with currency. Yet element number 28 is not a member of the group known as the 'coinage metals' (that privilege is reserved for group 11, which contains copper, silver and gold), and neither is it the main constituent of the US 5-cent coin (known as a 'nickel'); again, copper is the winner there, making up 75 percent of a 'nickel'.

Electron configuration: 2.8.16.2

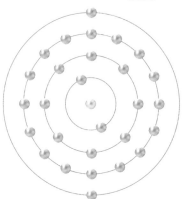

⊙ *The modern US 'nickel' coin is in fact made primarily from copper and not element number 28.*

Like its periodic table neighbour cobalt, nickel has its origins in the mining communities of eighteenth-century Germany. Once again, German miners failed to extract copper from an ore that they thought contained copper, but actually did not. Superstitiously, they blamed their failure on the Devil himself, and used the word *Kupfernickel* (literally 'copper Devil') to describe the bothersome, non-copper-yielding ore. When a new metal – nickel – was finally extracted from the same ore, it took its name from the original German expression of frustration.

Weird alloys

Nickel may be the most interesting and versatile of all the transition metals when it comes to the alloys that it makes. There is a wide array of them, and they exhibit some curious properties, with most of the important ones revolving around a resistance to corrosion and an ability to continue to perform well at high temperatures. One such remarkable alloy is Invar. The name Invar is derived from the word 'invariable', which is a clue to its most important property. When heated, unlike other metals, Invar hardly expands *at all*. The Swiss physicist who discovered it, Charles Édouard Guillaume (1861–1938), won the 1920 Nobel Pr in Physics for 'the service he has rendered to precision measurements in Physics by his discovery of anomalies in nickel steel alloys'. Invar is an alloy of nickel and iron, and is one of a family of metals that also includes Elinvar. Again the name is derived from the most important property of the alloy, this time the fact that it is elastically invariable, meaning that it resists a change of shape when a force is applied. Invar and Elinvar have each found uses in instruments where precision is important: for example, in watch springs and various gauges. Their ability to be consistent over both time and temperature ranges ensures the continued accuracy of the instruments.

Another alloy of nickel, this time in an approximately 50:50 ratio with titanium and known as nitinol, has a different, incredible

Ⓐ *A nickel nodule alongside a block of purified nickel metal. Nickel is found on earth with sulfur and iron in the mineral pentlandite.*

property. Known for being a shape-memory metal, when deformed, nitinol can spring back to its original shape. One of its most popular uses has been in the production of frames for eyewear. Developed in the late 1950s and early 1960s by engineers at the Naval Ordnance Laboratory in Maryland, USA, the alloy takes its name from the elements that make it up, and the place where it was discovered: *Ni*ckel *Ti*tanium-*N*aval *O*rdnance *L*aboratory.

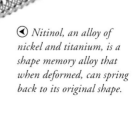

Ⓐ *Nitinol, an alloy of nickel and titanium, is a shape memory alloy that when deformed, can spring back to its original shape.*

Cu Copper

Chemical symbol	Cu
Atomic number	29
Atomic mass	63.546
Boiling point	2562 °C (5301 °F)
Melting point	1084.62 °C (1984.32 °F)

Copper's raw colour sets it apart from many of the other metallic elements, most of which are silvery, whitish or grey. In both its pure metallic form (the familiar brownish-red colour), and in the form of the vivid green patina, a combination of various compounds of copper, such as the carbonate and the chloride (as seen on the weathered exterior of the iconic Statue of Liberty watching over New York harbour), there is just no mistaking it.

Electron configuration:
2.8.18.1

At the top of group 11 of the periodic table, copper is the first of the group of elements known as the coinage metals. In reality, the number of metals that are used in the manufacture of coins extends far beyond copper, gold and silver, and incorporates well over two dozen of the chemical elements. However, because copper is another element of antiquity, it assumes particular historical importance. Copper and its alloys have been known for thousands of years, with bronze (see tin, pp. 108–109) and brass (see zinc, pp. 60–61) being some of the most well-known and important. In terms of coins, another alloy is more important in modern times than both of those. The combination of copper and nickel (unsurprisingly known as cupronickel) has been in widespread use for coins all over the world.

In the UK, coins known as 'silver' for their colour were actually made from the copper and nickel alloy for a number of years. Interestingly, the constitution of coins is subject to change as the market price for metals varies over time.

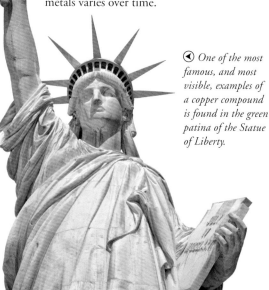

◀ *One of the most famous, and most visible, examples of a copper compound is found in the green patina of the Statue of Liberty.*

Conductivity and resistivity

In its pure metal form, copper is an extraordinarily good conductor of electricity as well as being malleable and ductile. This combination of properties has made it a popular metal in applications such as electrical wiring. Its ability to resist attack by both water and air, along with its relatively non-toxic nature when compared to lead, means that it is now the premier metal used to make water pipes.

Copper's excellent conductivity has long been exploited for electrical wiring.

Blue-blooded

Copper is an essential metal for humans in homeostatic processes, and a lack of it can cause various neurological disorders. Problems can occur following surgery, in particular those involving the stomach, where the disruption of the body can lead to difficulties in absorbing the metal. In animals, copper is also essential, and in one of those essential roles it affords

certain invertebrates (such as horseshoe crabs and some snails) one interesting characteristic: it makes their blood blue. The explanation lies in a biochemical molecule called haemocyanin, which is analogous to haemoglobin (see iron, pp. 52–53) in human blood. In haemocyanin the metal at the centre of the compound is not iron, but copper. This important difference means that the animals have blue rather than red blood.

Some creatures, such as the horseshoe crab, have 'blue' blood. This is caused by the haemoglobin analogue haemocyanin, in which the former's iron ions are replaced by copper ions.

Zn Zinc

Chemical symbol	Zn
Atomic number	30
Atomic mass	65.38
Boiling point	907 °C (1665 °F)
Melting point	419.53 °C (787.15 °F)

Electron
configuration: 2.8.18.2

As a metal, zinc is reactive, has a low melting point, and is relatively cheap, all of which add to its versatility. Whether it be at the literal heart of a US 1-cent piece (the coin has a core made of almost pure zinc encased in a copper shell), or being used as a sacrificial anode to save another metal from corrosion, zinc gets around.

⊙ *Zinc metal has a typical silvery grey colour. It is often found in the same deposits as lead and silver.*

Zinc is another element with its roots firmly in antiquity and without a specific discoverer *per se*. Known by the ancient civilisations in the form of its most famous alloy, brass, several sources cite the first isolation of the pure metal by German chemist Andreas Marggraf (1709–1782) in 1746 as the point that marks the true birth of element 30.

Zinc sits at the top of group 12, and is the final d-block element in the fourth row of the periodic table. Its classification as a transition metal is debatable, and indeed, in terms of at least one definition of transition metals, completely wrong. If one uses the definition of transition metals as those elements that form stable ions that have partially filled d-subshells then, like scandium, which forms an ion with an entirely empty d-subshell, zinc's 2+ ion disqualifies it, since in that ion, zinc has a completely filled d-subshell.

▲ *Galvanised steel is a popular construction material that harnesses zinc's reactivity to sacrificially protect the steel from corrosion.*

Galvanization

Zinc's relatively high reactivity is what makes it so useful to humans. In situations where it is desirable to prevent another metal from reacting, zinc can be placed adjacent to that metal, and the zinc will react preferentially. This is exactly what happens when steel is galvanised. Not only does the layer of zinc protect the steel underneath it, but even if that protective layer is damaged and the steel exposed, it's still the zinc that will corrode before the iron in the steel. In marine situations, ship hulls made from iron can be protected in a similar manner by simply having a large mass of zinc bolted to the structure, where once again, zinc's higher reactivity will intervene to save the iron.

▶ *Redox reactions involve the transfer of electrons from one species to another. In the reaction of zinc metal with copper ions, the zinc transfers two electrons to the copper ions.*

Redox reactions

Zinc's ability to act as a sacrificial metal is due to a type of chemical reaction where electrons are exchanged, known as a redox reaction. Such a reaction helps to explain another popular use of zinc, as a component of batteries. All batteries work on the same principle: that one of the components will release electrons, and that the other will receive those same charged particles. As the electrons flow, electricity is generated, and the battery releases its power. In batteries, zinc, whether used in conjunction with carbon, or nickel, or even air, is the anode, where it is the species that releases the electrons that travel to the other component, known as the cathode.

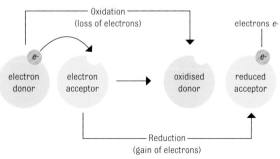

Y Yttrium

Chemical symbol	Y
Atomic number	39
Atomic mass	88.906
Boiling point	3345 °C (6053 °F)
Melting point	1522 °C (2771.60 °F)

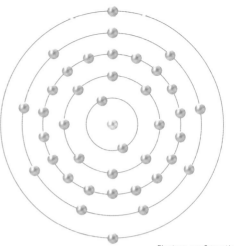

Electron configuration:
2.8.18.9.2

The very name of element number 39 suggests to some a bizarre, esoteric nature, but actually it can be explained quite easily. Yttrium is one of four elements named after a single, otherwise insignificant place. Why? Well, the metal is one of four elements – along with terbium (65), erbium (68), and ytterbium (70) – that were originally sourced from the mineral yttria, which was found in a mine in the small town of Ytterby, Sweden.

Rare or transition?

As a transition metal (or is it?), yttrium is a dark grey solid with a melting point of over 1,500 °C (2,732 °F). The question as to whether yttrium should be classified as a transition metal or not is tied up in its similarity to the lanthanoids, formerly known as the rare earth elements. Ironically, most of those elements are not rare at all, but they are notoriously difficult to separate from one another, and therefore very difficult to identify. Yttrium was the first of the 'rare' earths to be identified, at the end of the eighteenth century. The actual date of its discovery by Johan Gadolin (1760–1852) is a little vague, since at that time there were no well-established protocols for reporting such things. Gadolin probably identified yttrium a few years before his officially published paper on the matter in 1794.

◄ *Yttrium iron garnet, or YIG, has a number of specialist acoustic and optical applications.*

Super-cold superconductor

Yttrium's applications are fairly specialised. It is certainly a useful element in a number of situations but, like its name, many of them feel a little obscure. For example, a compound of yttrium that includes barium, copper and oxygen is a superconductor that works at temperatures of around −182 °C (−269 °F), or approximately 91 kelvin. Believe it or not, that's considered a relatively high temperature for superconductors, with most functioning at much lower temperatures still. Such superconducting material is plunged into liquid nitrogen to achieve the necessary ultracold conditions. The yttrium compound's chemical formula is usually reported as $YBa_2Cu_3O_7$, but the actual number of oxygen atoms can vary a little. That formula is rather striking in and of itself, and the compound has become known by two other, intriguing monikers: 'YBCO' and '1-2-3', the latter being a reference to the ratio of Y, Ba and Cu atoms in the structure.

Did you say yin and yang?

Continuing the fast and loose use of chemical nomenclature, we find two more interesting yttrium compounds. YIG (yttrium iron garnet) and YAG (yttrium aluminium garnet) are two pretty weird compounds that also have very specialised applications. YIG – which is actually a compound of yttrium, iron and oxygen – has several interesting optical and acoustic properties, which include its ability to act as a filter for microwaves. YAG – this time yttrium in conjunction with aluminium and oxygen – has found use as a synthetic gemstone. It can be manufactured to resemble a diamond, and can be coloured easily by the addition of other elements such as neodymium (pink) and cobalt (blue).

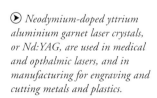 *Neodymium-doped yttrium aluminium garnet laser crystals, or Nd:YAG, are used in medical and opthalmic lasers, and in manufacturing for engraving and cutting metals and plastics.*

Zr Zirconium

Chemical symbol	Zr
Atomic number	40
Atomic mass	91.224
Boiling point	4409 °C (7968 °F)
Melting point	1855 °C (3371 °F)

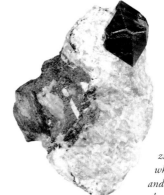

◀ *A sample of zircon, essentially zirconium silicate, from which zirconium metal and zirconium dioxide can be extracted.*

Zirconium is a brutally hard metal, with a reputation for being a tough cookie. It is used as an industrial abrasive, but element number 40 is better known for another application where its hardness is utilised: as a diamond substitute, in the form of cubic zirconium (and zirconium's discovery is linked to diamonds, too). No matter where one finds zirconium, it is one durable customer.

When the German chemist Martin Heinrich Klaproth (1743–1817) was investigating a sample of jargon (a form of zircon, a diamond-like gemstone) in 1789, he extracted the oxide of a hitherto unknown element. It took a while to isolate the element itself – that didn't happen until 1824 when Jöns Jacob Berzelius (1779–1848) managed to extract it – and it even confounded the brilliant Davy (see page 16) and his electrolysis experiments of 1808.

▶ *Zirconia crowns are common in modern dentistry. Known as EZR, these ceramic crowns have superior strength and are resistant to corrosion.*

Ceramic strength

As the pure element zirconium is nothing more than a typical silver-coloured, shiny metal, but in many of its most important applications it looks very different. The element appears as the component of a number of ceramic materials, notably as zirconia, or zirconium dioxide, ZrO_2. In this ceramic form it has a number of applications related to its heat resistance and lack of chemical reactivity, such as its use in dentistry, and as a substitute for stainless steel in ceramic knives and industrial cutting tools.

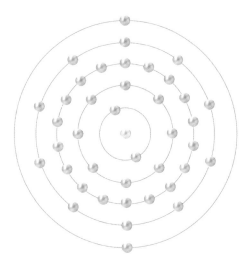

Electron configuration:
2.8.18.10.2

Counterintuitive

Every now and then one will find an element or one of its compounds that defies conventional wisdom. If you ask most people, even those without a working knowledge of chemistry or physics, what happens to the physical size of objects when they are heated, most will answer that they expand. This is, of course, largely true, but there is one odd compound of zirconium that does not comply. Zirconium tungstate, ZrW_2O_8, has a crystalline structure that does exactly the opposite when heated: it shrinks! It is possible that future uses of such 'negative thermal expansion materials' could be in composites, where a combination of negative and positive thermal expansion may result in a net zero thermal expansion.

Disabling deadly gas

In 2015, scientists at Northwestern University, Illinois, USA, reported an amazing property of another zirconium compound, one that could have a big impact on geopolitics in the future. Metal-organic frameworks (MOFs) contain metals combined with organic compounds. One particular MOF has zirconium as part of its structure, and the compound has been shown to be capable of disabling Soman (or GD), a ferocious and deadly nerve gas. The zirconium MOF is a porous material that can trap the gas within its structure and, by catalysing a chemical conversion that converts it into a harmless compound, render it ineffective. It is hoped that the technology might be put to use in disabling stockpiles of chemical weapons.

⊙ A sarin rocket being dismantled in 1990. A more modern process may use MOFs to disable chemical weapons.

Nb Niobium

Chemical symbol	Nb
Atomic number	41
Atomic mass	92.906
Boiling point	4744 °C (8571 °F)
Melting point	2477 °C (4491 °F)

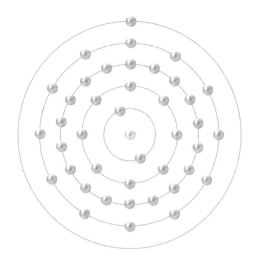

Electron configuration:
2.8.18.12.1

Another element with a complex history of discovery, and in this case, a complicated history of naming too, the controversy around element number 41 has, since 1950, settled down a bit. It was not until the middle of the twentieth century that the IUPAC formally gave it its modern name of niobium, forcing everyone who was still using the old name of columbium (with the old chemical symbol Cb), to fall into line.

Greek roots

The element's new name is derived from Niobe, who in Greek mythology was the daughter of Tantalus. At this point it is worth taking a quick look at the periodic table and making a note of the element directly underneath niobium: number 73, tantalum. Niobium had actually been discovered in 1801, nearly 150 years before it was named in the

modern sense. Found in a mineral called columbite, the connection to tantalum is no accident, since the two elements are often found together in nature as well as lying next to one another on the periodic table.

Hot and cold

In a 1970 article in the American Chemistry Society's magazine *Chemistry*, niobium was described as a 'space age metal'. The article discussed many applications of niobium, including its use as a superconductor and its combination with other metals in a range of alloys. It also mentioned superconducting magnets, which have since become incredibly important in both

◄ Like many elements, niobium's name has ancient roots. It derives from Niobe, the daughter of Tantalus in Greek mythology.

medicine and science. Superconducting niobium-containing magnets can be found at the centre of magnetic resonance imaging (MRI) used for medical diagnosis, and in particle accelerators, including the Large Hadron Collider (LHC) near Geneva, in Switzerland. In the LHC, the magnets are held at single-digit Kelvin temperatures, and can produce extraordinarily strong magnetic fields, up to 2,000 times stronger than a typical household magnet. At the other end of the temperature spectrum, niobium's high melting point, shared with similar metals such as tantalum, made it an early choice for the filaments of incandescent lightbulbs, before it was superseded by a metal with an even higher melting point, tungsten (see pp. 86–87).

Kaleidoscope of colours

One visually stunning use of niobium has been in the manufacture of coins. The Austrian mint has produced a number of euro denomination coins with brightly coloured centres surrounded by silver-coloured rings. The coins are truly beautiful, and are created by utilising an interesting property of niobium metal. When it is anodised – a process that produces an oxide layer on the surface of the metal – it is found that varying the voltage used in the process causes different thicknesses of niobium oxides to be formed. These different thicknesses cause differing degrees of

⊛ *The Large Hadron Collider (LHC) at CERN, on the border of France and Switzerland, utilises niobium-containing magnets.*

light diffraction that in turn produce some extraordinarily vivid colours, notably greens, blues, purples, yellows, pinks and golds. The same process can be used to produce anodised jewellery made from niobium, with equally interesting results.

⊛ *The anodization of niobium can produce vivid hues, a property that has been exploited in the production of these colourful Austrian coins.*

Mo Molybdenum

Electron configuration:
2.8.18.13.1

Chemical symbol	Mo
Atomic number	42
Atomic mass	95.95
Boiling point	4639 °C (8382 °F)
Melting point	2623 °C (4753 °F)

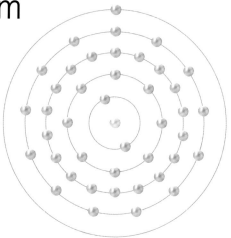

KEY FIGURE

CARL
WILHELM
SCHEELE

1742–86

Famously known as 'hard luck Scheele', a name given to him by the author and academic Isaac Asimov, Carl Wilhelm was indeed unfortunate. Through a combination of that misfortune, and not-quite-brilliant-enough chemistry, Scheele missed out on being credited with no less than six elements, possibly seven. The elements that slipped through his grasp were barium, chlorine, molybdenum, nitrogen, manganese, tungsten and most notably, oxygen.

Perhaps the element with the strangest-sounding name on the periodic table (although admittedly there are quite a few other candidates), molybdenum's moniker is derived from the Greek *molybdos*, meaning 'lead'. Molybdenite, the chief ore of molybdenum, is a soft, black substance that is similar to graphite. In fact, molybdenite's similarity to graphite is so strong that, like its carbon analogue, it has been used both as a lubricant and as the 'lead' in pencils.

Molybdenite's heat resistance is useful since alternative lubricants, such as oils, break down at high temperatures, rendering them useless. So how exactly did element number 42 become associated with lead? To answer this we must look back to molybdenite once more, and its similarity to other materials. It was found that molybdenite (molybdenum disulfide, MoS_2), was almost identical to galena, lead(II) sulfide, PbS, from which lead was extracted. Molybdenite was a tricky mineral to fully analyse and it took several years and several chemists to sort it all out. After work by Carl Willhelm Scheele (1742–86) and Peter Jacob Hjelm (1746–1813), the new element was finally identified in 1781.

Moly alloys

Molybdenum's chief and most important uses in the modern world revolve around the production of so-called 'moly steels'. When alloyed with iron and carbon, molybdenum produces steels that are significantly harder and more temperature-resistant than ones that do not contain the transition element. Even very small amounts of molybdenum, totalling only a few percent of the material's total mass, can dramatically increase the strength of the alloy.

Isotope shortages

Technetium-99m, a metastable isotope of technetium, is used in medical imaging (see pp. 70–71). Tc-99m is produced from the nuclear decay of Mo-99, so the former's production is dependent upon a steady supply of the latter. For many years the required molybdenum has been farmed from nuclear facilities, where it is a by-product of fission reactions of uranium. However, in September 2016 the US National Academies of Sciences, Engineering and Medicine released a report stating that the medical field could face severe shortages of both isotopes, due to a number of key nuclear facilities either shutting down

completely, or scaling back production during maintenance. With such a widespread and important use of the isotopes in medicine, this presents a real problem for the future.

Mass loss

Molybdenum exists as a number of isotopes that range in mass from 94 to 100 atomic mass units. The relative abundances of molybdenum's isotopes (and indeed those of all of the elements) are used in a calculation that determines the atomic weight of the element, and that is the number that appears along with the atomic number on the periodic table. The abundances of isotopes are relatively well known, and remain fairly constant, but from time to time there can be discoveries of new sources of elements that upset the currently understood ratios of the isotopes. In 2013, the IUPAC released amended atomic weights for nineteen of the elements. Not only was molybdenum one of the elements that needed its atomic mass to be amended, it was the element whose average mass decreased by the greatest extent, from 95.96 to 95.95.

⊙ *Molybdenum is a hard, silver-grey-coloured metal that has a very high melting point. Molybdenite is the chief ore from which the element is extracted.*

Tc Technetium

Chemical symbol	Tc
Atomic number	43
Atomic mass	98 (most stable isotope)
Boiling point	4265 °C (7709 °F)
Melting point	2157 °C (3915 °F)

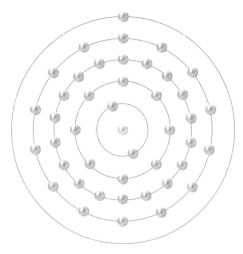

Electron configuration:
2.8.18.14.1

When Mendeleev predicted that an element (which he called eka-manganese) with an atomic weight of 100 would one day be discovered, little did he know that it would prove to be a huge headache for future chemists to find. Technetium was named after the Greek *tekhnetos*, meaning 'artificial', since upon its isolation in 1937 it became the first artificially manufactured element.

To spoil that story just a little, it was later discovered that minuscule amounts of element 43 can be found in nature, where it is a product of the radioactive decay of naturally occurring uranium. These amounts are so small, however, and the technetium isotopes so unstable, that the amount of naturally occurring technetium is generally considered to be effectively zero. Because of the very tiny amount of technetium that is found naturally, the element proved to be a tremendously difficult one to track down. The Italian duo of Emilio Segrè (1905–1989) and Carlo Perrier (1886–1948) finally discovered the element in samples of molybdenum from the cyclotron (the circular particle accelerator) at the University of California. Prior to that,

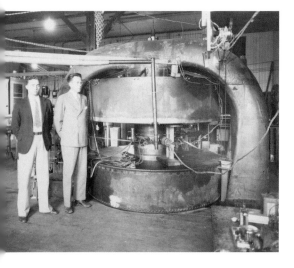

◀ *Technetium was discovered in samples of molybdenum from the cyclotron at the old Radiation Laboratory at the University of California, Berkeley, in 1937.*

several claims were made of its discovery, and it was erroneously given a number of names by those that claimed priority (a word used to describe the assignment of discovery of new elements). Among the names that were applied to samples that were thought to be technetium but later proved spurious were davyum and masurium. Given Humphry Davy's (see p. 16) colossal contributions to the discovery of elements, some (including the author) might think it's a great shame that davyum didn't stick to at least one element on the periodic table. As for masurium, it was a name given to what was thought to be the first sample of element 43 by the German trio of Ida Tacke (later Noddack) (1896–1978), Walter Noddack (1893–1960) and Otto Berg (1873–1979) in 1925. Their claim was ultimately dismissed as also being without merit, but work that reproduced their experiments 75 years later suggested that perhaps they should have been credited. The truth of the matter was that between the First and Second World Wars, Germany's place in the geopolitical scene was not an easy one for some to stomach, and outward hostility lead to politics getting in the way of science on numerous occasions.

Seeing inside

Technetium's only significant use is in medical imaging where, in the form of the metastable isotope Tc-99m, its gamma ray emission is put to great use. The relatively short half-life of 6 hours means that the isotope can be injected into the body without fear of it hanging around for too long and causing damage. Only very tiny doses of the element are required, meaning that the radiation that the patient is exposed to remains very low. By using specially designed carriers, the radioactive isotope can be transported to certain organs in the body, including the heart, where specially designed cameras can detect the gamma radiation and produce images of the organ. Those images can help doctors to determine whether the organ is working correctly.

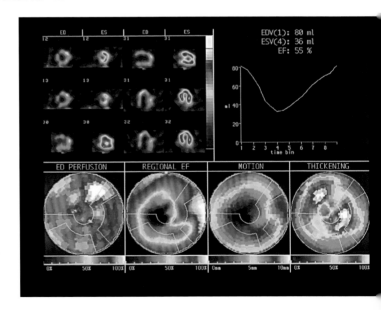

▶ The radioactive isotope technetium-99m is used in medical imaging, and can be sent, via specially designed transporters, to specific areas of the body, such as the brain and heart.

Ru Ruthenium

Chemical symbol	Ru
Atomic number	44
Atomic mass	101.07
Boiling point	4150 °C (7502 °F)
Melting point	2334 °C (4233 °F)

Ruthenium was named after the historical region of Ruthenia (part of modern-day Russia, Belarus and Ukraine), which was home to its discoverer, Karl Karlovich Klaus (1796–1864). Some sources, however, credit Gottfried Wilhelm Osann (1796–1866) with the discovery. His initial work investigating a platinum ore led to him make a claim that he had found three new metals; the only one that was ultimately confirmed was ruthenium.

A new type of 'group'?

The word 'group' has a very specific meaning when it comes to chemistry and the periodic table, and it is a pretty simple definition to understand. A group is a vertical column in the table of elements, for example, group 17, the halogens: fluorine, chlorine, bromine, iodine, astatine and tennessine. But ruthenium is part of a collection of elements that takes that formal designation and (somewhat unhelpfully) twists it into a new meaning. As one of the collection of elements known as the platinum group, ruthenium sits with rhodium, palladium, platinum, osmium and iridium right at the centre of the periodic table, in anything but a simple vertical column.

Ultimate prize

It is as a catalyst that ruthenium finds fame. In fact, in 2005 ruthenium was at the centre of the ultimate in chemistry fame, when Yves Chauvin (1930–2015), Robert Grubbs (b. 1942), and Richard Shrock (b. 1945) won the Nobel Prize in Chemistry 'for the development of the metathesis method in organic synthesis'. An important reaction in the manufacture of pharmaceuticals and polymers, the rearrangement of the organic groups surrounding the carbon-to-carbon double bonds in alkenes can be catalysed

◉ *Ruthenium is a relatively rare metal, with only a few tons produced each year. As a so-called 'platinum group' metal, it has much in common with Rh, Pd, Pt, Ir, and Os.*

by a ruthenium compound. The so-called Grubbs catalysts are highly selective (meaning that they are precise), and highly stable (meaning that they work under a number of different, extreme conditions).

Ruthenium has been proposed as a replacement catalyst for iron in the Haber process, which is used to manufacture ammonia on a massive scale worldwide.

More catalysts

In another critically important industrial process – the manufacture of ammonia, NH_3, for fertilisers – a different metal, iron, is used as a catalyst. The process, which takes nitrogen and hydrogen gas and converts it to NH_3, uses huge amounts of energy, and any small change in the efficiency of the catalyst could make a huge difference to the overall cost. This is not a small-scale operation; in 2012 it was estimated that almost 154 million tons of ammonia were produced globally, with around 85 percent of it being used to make fertilisers. Seen in that light, catalysts are important in terms of pure economics. So what does this have to do with ruthenium? Well, it has been floated as a potential replacement for iron. The ruthenium catalysts have been found to be more efficient, which would be tremendously helpful, but, as a relatively scarce metal, it is currently just too expensive to replace the traditional, less interesting catalyst on a large scale.

Electron configuration:
2.8.18.15.1

Rh Rhodium

Chemical symbol	Rh
Atomic number	45
Atomic mass	102.91
Boiling point	3695 °C (6683 °F)
Melting point	1964 °C (3567 °F)

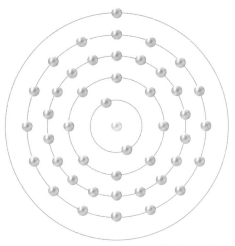

Electron configuration:
2.8.18.16.1

Rhodium is named after the Greek *rhodon,* **meaning rose-coloured. William Hyde Wollaston (1766–1828) first extracted a sample of reddish-pink rhodium chloride in 1803. It was obtained from a sample of impure platinum that was dissolved in a combination of acids (see osmium, pp. 90–91), and with it, three other new elements were also identified, namely, palladium, osmium and iridium.**

ⓥ *The honeycomb-like structure of many catalysts serves to increase the surface area available to the reactants, thus helping to speed the reaction.*

Rhodium is routinely quoted on the metal markets as one of the most expensive commodities on earth. Its scarcity is central to its high cost, but it also helps that as a pure metal, rhodium is relatively inert and therefore super-resistant to corrosion. Because of that property it is shiny, and it is used as a reflective surface in high-performance optical mirrors. More usually, much like its periodic table neighbour to the left, ruthenium, rhodium's chemistry is largely tied up in the world of ultra-expensive catalysts, and the role that they play in industrial and research processes.

Start me up

These catalytic actions are often hidden away, either in industrial plants – for example, where rhodium catalysts are used in the manufacture of nitric acid and menthol – or perhaps on the underside of your car – where rhodium is a popular metal in the somewhat more mundane catalytic converter. Rhodium catalysts are so important in industry

Catalyst

Toxic gases such as carbon monoxide, nitrogen oxide and hydrocarbons, enter the converter

Less harmful substances, such as carbon dioxide and water, are released

▲ *The action of a catalytic converter in a car exhaust system helps to minimise the expulsion of harmful gases into the atmosphere, by converting pollutants in exhaust fumes to less harmful substances.*

that they have played a part in the award of multiple Nobel Prizes in Chemistry: once in 2001, when Japanese chemist Ryoji Noyori (b. 1938) was recognised for his work in the field, and again in 2007 (see pp. 94–95).

The role of rhodium in the automobile catalytic converter is its most important one, with the vast majority of rhodium produced in the world going into this application. Along with other platinum group metals, it aids the action of the device as a three-way converter (TWC), where three unwanted by-products of the internal combustion engine can be removed: carbon monoxide can be converted to carbon dioxide, hydrocarbons can be combusted to carbon dioxide and water, and NO_x (where x is a variable number) gases can be converted to N_2 and O_2.

Images of atoms

In a roundabout way, rhodium also played an important role in the early advancement of the nanotechnology of today. In the early 1980s, researchers at IBM's Almaden Research Center in San Jose, California, invented the first scanning tunnelling microscope, or STM.

The work eventually led to the 1986 Nobel Prize in Physics for its inventors. The microscope's relevance to chemistry lies in its ability to allow scientists to see images of individual molecules and atoms. The first images of molecules adsorbed on to the surface of metal were produced in 1988, when benzene was placed onto the surface of, you've guessed it, rhodium.

▼ *Rhodium played a part in the development of the scanning tunnelling microscope, which allows imaging at the atomic level.*

Pd Palladium

Chemical symbol	Pd
Atomic number	46
Atomic mass	106.42
Boiling point	5365 °F (2963 °C)
Melting point	2830.82 °F (1554.9 °C)

It is entirely appropriate that palladium sits next to rhodium, since the pair were discovered together, by the same person, and in the same impure sample of platinum. What sets palladium apart from most other elements is the very odd way that it was announced to the world by its discoverer, and the spat that it induced between him and a rival chemist.

Strange announcement

William Hyde Wollaston announced his discovery of palladium in a very peculiar manner. Rather than publishing his findings in a respected scientific journal in the accepted manner, he decided to advertise the element for sale in a London shop, where it was described on nothing more than a paper flyer.

Wollaston's motivation was that he wanted to profit from the sale of the metal, and by keeping it shrouded in mystery and secrecy, he thought he might have a better chance of doing just that. Irish chemist Richard Chenevix (1774–1830) publicly chastised Wollaston and challenged the veracity of the alleged new metal. Unfortunately for Chenevix, the metal did prove to be the real deal, Wollaston won the day, and Chenevix lost all credibility in the process.

Cold fusion

Like rhodium, palladium's main use is in automobile catalytic converters. Those reactions are tremendously helpful, but it is element number 46's extraordinary interaction with hydrogen gas that is the subject of much speculation and research. First, let's consider the ability of palladium to absorb hydrogen gas. Palladium's structure of metal ions, packed tightly together in a regular, lattice-like arrangement, allows hydrogen gas to accumulate within the structure, where it nestles between atoms. In this way, a sample of palladium is capable of absorbing up to 900 times its own volume of hydrogen. As such, palladium has been

◀ *William Hyde Wollaston announced the discovery of palladium in a very odd way, which some decried as unethical.*

proposed as a storage material for hydrogen gas, which would allow the gas to be transported without the need for high pressure, and to then be recovered from the solid as needed.

Electron configuration: 2.8.18.18

Hydrogen storage is great, but cold fusion is where palladium's interaction with hydrogen gets really interesting. If you want real controversy in science, then cold fusion is a great place to start!

The sun creates energy by fusing together hydrogen nuclei to make helium. This process takes place at super-high temperatures. But what if we could perform essentially the same reaction on earth, with a small electric current, so that the chemical reaction generated more energy than was used? Answer: the world's energy problems would be no more! This was essentially the claim made in 1989 by Martin Fleischmann (1927–2012) and Stanley Pons (b. 1943), when they introduced the world to the cold (or at least room-temperature) fusion of hydrogen atoms in an electrolytic cell with a palladium cathode. The research was quickly debunked when others could not replicate the production of energy that they reported, but the controversy rages on, with some still holding out hope that cold fusion might be real – with palladium at its heart.

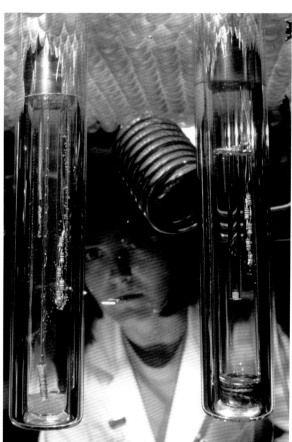

▶ *Experiments in cold fusion involve the electrolysis of water in a cell with a palladium cathode.*

77

Ag Silver

Chemical symbol	Ag
Atomic number	47
Atomic mass	107.87
Boiling point	2162 °C (3924 °F)
Melting point	961.78 °C (1763.2 °F)

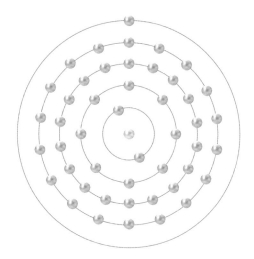

Electron configuration: 2.8.18.18.1

Silver sits below copper (the first element in group 11) and above gold (the third), which positions silver firmly in second place. This seems to fit nicely with silver's placement among the Olympic medal metals, especially when one realises that bronze is an alloy of copper. Despite apparently being destined for a permanent spot as a runner-up, silver does excel in some respects.

As one of the ancient elements, silver has been known to civilisations for thousands of years. In the form of coins and jewellery, it has been around since at least 3000 BCE. Like its close cousin gold, silver is a shiny metal that can be found as the free metal, but unlike gold, it rarely is. Silver has a greater tendency to react, and as such, element number 47 did not really come into the ancients' consciousness until some significant time after its more sparkly relation.

Let's reflect for a moment

Silver is among the most reflective of the metals (it depends on the wavelength of the incident light as to which metal is the best in any particular circumstance), so it is often used as the reflective surface for mirrors. However, where silver takes first place hands down is in its ability to conduct electricity. The first three elements in group 11 – silver, with its group mates copper and gold – are together the best conductors of electricity of all the elements in the periodic table.

⊙ *Most 'silver' jewellery is in fact not pure silver at all, but an alloy of silver and copper. A stamp of '925' indicates that the piece is 92.5 percent silver.*

Tarnish

With several desirable properties, silver is let down in only one regard, and it is quite an important one where aesthetics are concerned: silver tarnishes quickly, and quite badly. The tarnish is fairly simple to remove and the metal can easily be restored to its former glory, but the buildup of the familiar black discolouration of silver sulfide on the surface of fancy cutlery and other decorative ware has certainly held silver back when compared to, say, gold. It is this tendency to corrode that also has gold beating silver in the production of electrical contacts that must stay pristine.

One area where the darkening of silver compounds has been put to constructive use is in photography, where silver ions in the +1 oxidation state, typically in silver halides such as silver bromide $AgBr$, are reduced to silver metal when exposed to light, causing the darkening that creates the photographic image.

Feeling better?

Silver has had an interesting role in medicine over the centuries, too, in particular as the compound silver nitrate. $AgNO_3$ has turned up in a number of medical applications, including as an antiseptic and as a wart remover. Some alternative therapies have promoted colloidal silver as a veritable cure-all, but its effectiveness is highly debatable and side effects are likely to outweigh any benefit. In 1999, the US Food and Drug Administration (FDA) effectively banned over-the-counter silver-containing products that make any claim relating to health benefits. An interesting and somewhat alarming side effect of ingesting too much silver is a condition known as argyria. This leads to a bizarre discolouration of the skin, with the sufferer literally turning a greyish-blue colour.

(▶) Boulevard du Temple *was made by Daguerre in 1838 and is thought to be the oldest photograph that includes an image of a living person. The daguerrotype process used sheets of silver-plated copper.*

Cd Cadmium

Chemical symbol	Cd
Atomic number	48
Atomic mass	112.41
Boiling point	767 °C (1413 °F)
Melting point	321.07 °C (609.93 °F)

A wicked element, cadmium is associated with two of its group 12 mates, zinc and mercury. Like mercury, cadmium is an insidious poison, and as such extremely dangerous; whenever zinc is mined, you can expect some additional, unwelcome, cadmium coming along for the ride. That's a real problem if the cadmium is consumed.

⊙ *Smithsonite is an ore of zinc that can take on different colours depending on its chemical composition. Cadmium impurities give a yellowish hue.*

Off-colour

Cadmium has a rich history of use in pigments in the art world, but unfortunately its toxicity is problematic. As a poison, cadmium can at best certainly make you feel off-colour, and at worst can kill you. But an odd colour was the key to cadmium's initial discovery. Cadmia was a mineral popularly used to produce zinc oxide in Germany in the early part of the nineteenth century. By heating the mineral, which is essentially zinc carbonate, it yields carbon dioxide and what should be a residue of white zinc oxide. Friedrich Stromeyer (1776–1835) was a bureaucrat charged with overseeing the pharmacies in Hannover at the time. He was confused over the formation of a yellowish tinge that persisted in the oxide, when the product should have been pure white. In 1817 he identified a new element, which he called cadmium after the original name for the zinc carbonate mineral.

Ouch, ouch!

Japan has an unfortunate history of environmental pollution and subsequent disease caused by group 12 elements, as we shall see in the case of mercury and the poisoning at Minamata (pp. 98–99). Shamefully, a similar incident is associated with the element directly above mercury in the periodic table. In the first half of the twentieth century, a high occurrence of a debilitating bone disease was noted in the Toyama Prefecture on the west coast of Japan. For several years prior to the disease being recognised as a problem, the Mitsui Mining and Smelting Co. had been releasing cadmium

waste into the local water supply. Downstream, local residents then used the water for the irrigation of rice fields, and the scene was set for a cadmium poisoning disaster. One of cadmium's insidious actions is its ability to mimic calcium. As such, it tends to accumulate in bones, where it can weaken their structure, soften them, and ultimately cause them to break far more easily than healthy ones. Other symptoms include kidney damage that can eventually lead to death.

The condition was known locally as *itai-itai* disease, since people afflicted were said to call out 'itai-itai!' – 'ouch, ouch!' – when the pain from their damaged skeletons became too great. The clean-up of the cadmium pollution was a huge

Ⓐ *Cadmium is often found in conjunction with zinc, so zinc mining can cause the release of toxic cadmium into the environment, as it has here, at Storey's Creek, Tasmania.*

project for the Japanese government, and between 1979 and 2012 they effectively replaced all of the soil in the affected area. This was such an enormous project that it took thirty-three years to complete.

The process will likely have some important lessons for a potential similar cleanup in the wake of the 2011 Fukushima nuclear accident (see caesium, pp. 22–23, strontium, pp. 34–35 and iodine, pp. 200–201).

Electron configuration:
2.8.18.18.2

Hf Hafnium

Chemical symbol	Hf
Atomic number	72
Atomic mass	178.49
Boiling point	4603 °C (8317 °F)
Melting point	2233 °C (4051 °F)

Hafnium is named after the Latin name for Copenhagen, Hafnia, since it is the city where it was first discovered, in 1923, by the Danish chemist Dirk Coster (1889–1950), working with his Hungarian colleague George de Hevesy (1885–1966). Hafnium was an elusive element, being the penultimate of the naturally occurring elements to be discovered, and only being ousted for the dubious title of 'hardest to find' by rhenium (see pp. 88–89).

Hafnium's discovery owes a lot to Henry Moseley's work on the atomic number, and its relationship to zirconium. When Moseley reordered the elements via atomic number, it became apparent that a number of elements were missing, and number 72 was among those.

Here's number 72. No, it isn't!

Hafnium atoms are almost identical to those of zirconium, element number 40. As a result, it proved difficult to isolate and find hafnium. That wasn't the only problem, either. As an element that sits on the boundary of the transition metals and the rare earth elements, the methodology that was best suited to discovering it was not all that clear. Ultimately, the element was identified via X-ray analysis, when it created lines in the spectrum that confirmed the existence of a new element. Where was the element found? Why, in a sample of zircon (zirconium silicate), of course! However, by that time, element number 72 had been spuriously 'discovered', and thus incorrectly named, multiple times, with such monikers as asium, celtium, euxenium, jargonium, and oceanium. In fact, according to the 2014

◀ *Hafnium was one of the elements discovered after Moseley's identification of atomic number. The element was named after the Latin name for Copenhagen, Hafnia.*

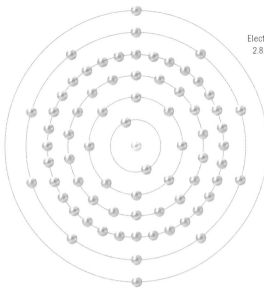

Electron configuration:
2.8.18.32.10.2

researchers at Brown University, Rhode Island, reported a compound with a melting point that they predicted would be over 4,100 °C (7,412 °F)! A blow for hafnium, you might think, but not so fast: this new compound also contains hafnium, this time combined with nitrogen and carbon.

Nuclear control

As a shiny, silver-coloured metal that is ultra-resistant to corrosion due to the oxide layer that it forms on its surface, hafnium is an important industrial element. With its high melting point of 2,230° C (4,046 °F), and its ability to absorb neutrons very well, it's a good candidate for use as control rods in nuclear reactors. By lowering the hafnium alloy rods into position, the nuclear chain reaction can be controlled. This comes at a price, though, since hafnium is a very expensive element.

book *The Lost Elements: The Periodic Table's Shadow Side*, by Marco Fontani, Mariagrazia Costa, and Mary Virginia Orna – which catalogues incorrect claims of the discovery of new elements – hafnium has the other dubious distinction of being the element that has been incorrectly identified most often!

Meltdown

Just like zirconium, its neighbour to the north on the periodic table, hafnium is also an incredibly tough element. Hafnium carbide, for example, a compound that hafnium makes with tantalum and carbon, has an amazingly high melting point of almost 4,000 °C (7,232 °F). For a long time this substance was considered to be the compound with the highest melting point, but in July 2015

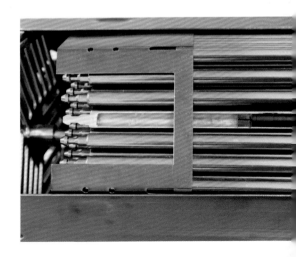

▶ *Hafnium plays an important role in nuclear reactors, where its ability to absorb neutrons allows it to control the chain reaction.*

Ta Tantalum

Chemical symbol	Ta
Atomic number	73
Atomic mass	180.95
Boiling point	5458 °C (9856 °F)
Melting point	3017 °C (5463 °F)

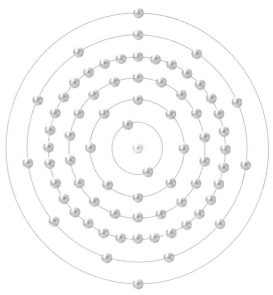

Electron configuration:
2.8.18.32.11.2

Another super-tough metal, tantalum is named after King Tantalus from Greek mythology. Its close relationship with niobium made it a tricky element to isolate. Just over one hundred years separate the first reporting of the new metal by Anders Ekeberg (1767–1813) in 1802 and its appearance as a pure element in 1903. Why such a long wait? Because separating it from the almost identical niobium proved very difficult.

Inside and outside the body

Like titanium, tantalum's resistance to corrosion means that it can be used for the manufacture of surgical instruments that are used outside the body, and as artificial surgical implants, such as synthetic joints, that are placed inside. As a component of some alloys, tantalum finds use in the aerospace industry as a component of jet engines and some external parts of rockets and other high-performance aircraft.

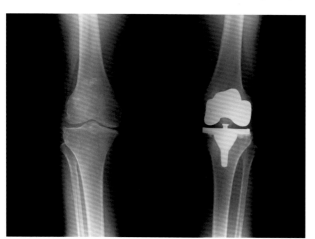

◀ *Tantalum is tough and resistant to corrosion, making it a great choice for surgical implants in the human body.*

An element of war and controversy

Tantalum's real power is found in its ability to conduct both electricity and heat incredibly well. This has led to its extensive use in capacitors, the tiny electronic components found in virtually every portable electronic device that anyone owns. Its durability, coupled with its superior electrical properties, means that tantalum can be made into tiny components that can store charge, but are at the same time mechanically strong enough to avoid damage. The capacitors are made not only from metallic tantalum, but also from the compound tantalum(V) oxide, Ta_2O_5.

⊙ *There is a rich supply of coltan, an ore from which tantalum is extracted, in the Democratic Republic of Congo, where exploitation of the mineral has fuelled conflict and led to a 'coltan crisis'.*

The unprecedented popularity of small mobile electronic devices has thrust tantalum into a position of some controversy. There are a few elements on the periodic table that are politically charged, and some of them are easy to guess. For example, it's not hard to work out that elements such as uranium and plutonium, which are used in nuclear weapons, might be politically sensitive, but others are less obvious. A sign outside the gorilla enclosure at the San Diego zoo reads thus: 'Since 2004, we have recycled almost 9,000 cell phones. This reduces the demand for Coltan, an ore used to make a component of cell phones, mined in gorilla habitat.' 'Coltan' is short for columbite–tantalite, an ore from which both niobium

and tantalum are extracted. Coltan is found in various parts of the world, but one particularly rich source is located in the Democratic Republic of Congo (DRC) in Central Africa. Civil war raged in the DRC from the late 1990s until 2003 (although conflict continues even today). In an attempt to fund their war efforts, multiple groups of antagonists, plus factions from neighbouring countries, exploited the natural resources found in the region via an illegal trade in coltan. In short, the conflict has given rise to a new phrase, 'blood tantalum', an unfortunate addition to the story of an otherwise pretty amazing element.

W Tungsten

Chemical symbol	W
Atomic number	74
Atomic mass	183.84
Boiling point	5555 °C (10031 °F)
Melting point	3422 °C (6192 °F)

⊙ *Tungsten's super-high melting point has been exploited in a number of applications, including in the glowing filaments of electric lightbulbs.*

Tough, dense, and with the highest melting point among all the elements, you can find tungsten in alloys and used in places where those attributes are likely to be important. Its high melting point was (and still is) the reason for its use as the glowing filaments in incandescent lightbulbs (see niobium, pp. 66–67, and osmium, pp. 90–91), and it has been used as a component of alloys on the business end of rockets, where temperatures can reach several thousand degrees Celsius.

Names and symbols

Perhaps the element with the most confusing chemical symbol on the periodic table (although potassium, silver, gold, mercury, antimony and others may have claims), tungsten has a reason for its apparent weirdness. The symbol comes from an alternative name for element number 74, wolfram, which in turn, comes from wolframite, an ore that contains tungsten… or wolfram! The discussion/controversy connected with element number 74's name has been a long and winding one, and has caused plenty of annoyance. The IUPAC's 'Red Book' (the bible of inorganic nomenclature) has been at the centre of it all, and IUPAC has some explaining to do. In 1783, the Spanish brothers Fausto (1755–1833) and Juan José Elhuyar (1754–96) had extracted tungsten from wolframite and, unsurprisingly, favoured the name wolfram for the new element. Unfortunately, prior to that, Carl Wilhelm Scheele had extracted the oxide of the same element from an ore called *tung sten* (Swedish for 'heavy stone'), so that name was also in use. For a couple of centuries both names persisted, and it was not until 1949 that the IUPAC attempted to clear up the confusion by choosing wolfram. Oddly, in 2005, the IUPAC abruptly erased all mentions of the name wolfram for element 74 from its Red Book, and tungsten replaced it. This caused much consternation, but the IUPAC insisted on tungsten from then on.

Searching for diamonds in the WC?

Tungsten finds further fame in compounds such as tungsten carbide, whose chemical formula is WC, and which therefore certainly has the potential for some juvenile amusement. WC was made accidentally by French chemist Henri Moissan (1852–1907), when he heated carbon with tungsten. He had been trying to manufacture diamonds by ferociously heating iron with charcoal, and he did have some success. However, the 'diamonds' that he produced were too small to be of any commercial value. When he tried the same method with other metals, including tungsten, he inadvertently created some fragments of the new, seriously hard, compound. He discarded them, but years later, German and American chemists perfected the art of manufacturing tungsten carbide. It is now a staple material used for drill bits and other cutting tools – ironically, often in applications where it

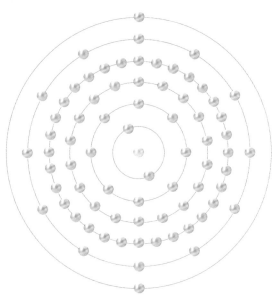

Electron configuration:
2.8.18.32.12.2

replaces diamonds. Throughout its history, tungsten carbide has found its way into the mundane and the profound. Products that have parts that need to be ultra-durable, such as the ball in a ballpoint pen, often contain it, as does armour-piercing ammunition.

▶ *From ballpoint pens (right) to armour-piercing ammunition, wherever super-tough materials are needed, tungsten carbide is a good choice.*

Re Rhenium

Chemical symbol	Re
Atomic number	75
Atomic mass	186.21
Boiling point	5596 °C (10105 °F)
Melting point	5596 °C (5767 °F)

Ahhh, rhenium! Is it the most romantic element on the periodic table? The story of its discovery undeniably has a certain charm. It was the last of all the naturally occurring elements to be found (as long as one considers technetium to be essentially absent from the earth's crust) and shortly after, two of its joint discoverers, Walter Karl Friedrich Noddack and Ida Eva Tacke, married one another.

(▶) *Ida Eva Tacke (later Ida Eva Noddack) not only gets credit, with her husband, for the discovery of rhenium, but she is generally credited with being the first scientist to consider the idea of nuclear fission.*

Mendeleev had predicted both rhenium and its northern neighbour on the periodic table, technetium, and at the time of the discovery of element 75, the same scientists believed that they had also discovered technetium. That discovery was eventually dismissed, but later studies suggested that they may have actually been correct, and that they should have been awarded priority. As we saw earlier (see technetium, pp. 70–71), priority for element 43 was ultimately given to another team, and at a later date.

Truly odd chemistry

From a pure chemistry point of view, rhenium has a couple of very odd properties. First, it is the element on the periodic table that exhibits the greatest number of oxidation states. The transition metals as a group are known for their ability to lose varying numbers of their s and d electrons, but no element does it quite like rhenium. It shows oxidation states +1 up to +7 (its most common state), zero, of course (since that is the oxidation state of any element in its elemental state), plus, bizarrely, −1. In another extraordinary piece of chemistry, in 1964 the American chemist Albert Cotton (1930–2007) confirmed something that was thought to be impossible at the time (although it had been hinted at previously):

The formation of a quadruple covalent bond. In the complex ion $[Re_2Cl_8]^{2-}$, two rhenium atoms are bonded to one another with four bonds. Although some other compounds containing such bonds have since been synthesised, it is a very unusual phenomenon.

Let's get physical

The outstanding properties of rhenium do not end with its chemical properties; it has some physical attributes that are pretty amazing, too. One of the rarest elements on earth, it is also one of the most dense (only osmium, iridium and platinum are more dense), and possesses one of the highest melting points (third behind only carbon and tungsten).

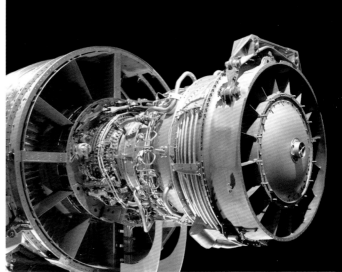

(A) *Some parts of jet engines, for example, the blades, are made from alloys that contain small amounts of rhenium.*

From Mo

Rhenium is not an easy metal to obtain, since its ores are very rare, but it has been extracted as an impurity from other processes involving molybdenum. Once it has been extracted, it finds use in high-performance alloys, and as a metal that can withstand high temperatures in electrical and industrial settings. As a transition metal, it is no surprise to learn that it also finds use as a catalyst, where a rhenium/platinum combination is used in the manufacture of gasoline.

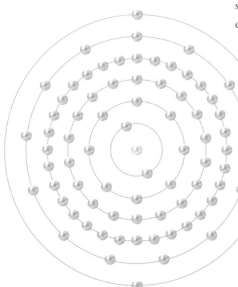

Electron configuration:
2.8.18.32.13.2

Os Osmium

Chemical symbol	Os
Atomic number	76
Atomic mass	190.23
Boiling point	5012 °C (9054 °F)
Melting point	3033 °C (5491 °F)

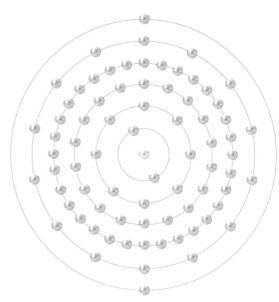

Electron configuration:
2.8.18.32.14.2

**Found with iridium – both physically
In the earth and at the time of its
discovery in 1803 – osmium will always
be linked to its periodic table neighbour
to the right. Named after the Greek
osme, meaning 'odour' or 'smell',
the moniker comes from the fact
that the element, along with some
of its compounds, stinks!**

The English chemist Smithson Tennant
(1761–1815) discovered osmium and
iridium in the residue from a platinum ore
that had been dissolved in aqua regia, the
same residue that led to the discovery of
palladium and rhodium for Wollaston. Aqua
regia deserves a special mention, since it was
a compound commonly used by chemists of
the time as they sought new elements and
substances. A combination of what we now
know as concentrated nitric and hydrochloric

acids, it had the ability to dissolve gold metal.
(This ability was put to good use by the
chemist George de Hevesy, who, it is thought,
used aqua regia to hide gold Nobel Prize
medals during the Nazi occupation of
Denmark, dissolving them and recovering
the metal later.)

▶ *Aqua regia is a concentrated solution of nitric and
hydrochloric acids that gained notoriety among early
chemists due to its ability to dissolve gold metal.*

Dense and light?

As well as usually being recorded as the most dense of all of the elements (there are methods of measurement that make its brother iridium the most dense), osmium also has a very high melting point of just over 3,000 °C (5,432 °F). With such a high melting point, element number 76 was used as a filament in the early days of the production of incandescent lightbulbs. At the same time, fellow period six transition element tungsten was also being used in the same way and for the same reason (it has a melting point approximately 400 °C (752 °F) higher than even osmium). At the beginning of the twentieth century, three German lighting companies merged with one another. Their names were Auergesellschaft, Siemens & Halske, and Allgemeine Elektrizitäts-Gesellschaft. These were hardly names that tripped off the tongue, so a new name was sought for the merged company. What better than to use the names of the two most popular elements for filaments at the time, and combine them into a snappy, new name? In Germany, and indeed in English-speaking countries, tungsten was then known as wolfram (see tungsten, pp. 86–87), so when merged with element number 76's name, the OSRAM company name was born.

◀ An early advertisement in French for lightbulbs produced by the OSRAM company.

Catalysts, alloys and nasty vapours

As an element, osmium's uses are limited to those that are usually associated with transition metals – as catalysts and in alloys. However, one of its most well-known compounds, osmium tetroxide, OsO_4, has a few interesting properties of its own. It is a volatile solid that sublimes, and an extremely toxic compound, which is damaging to the skin, lungs and in particular the eyes, where it can cause blindness. There was a time when osmium also had the highest oxidation state of any transition metal, coming in at a whopping +8, but in 2014, and in yet another connection to iridium, that claim to fame was lost (see iridium, pp. 92–93).

◀ A blueish-grey-coloured metal, osmium has an extraordinarily high density. It also exhibits an unusually large number of oxidation states.

Ir Iridium

Chemical symbol	Ir
Atomic number	77
Atomic mass	192.22
Boiling point	4428 °C (8002 °F)
Melting point	2446 °C (4435 °F)

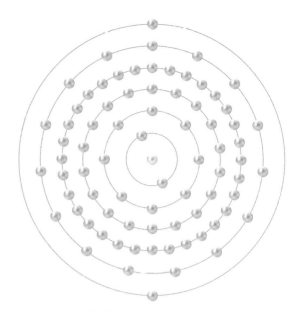

Electron configuration:
2.8.18.32.15.2

Here's the other half of the osmium–iridium tandem. Found by Smithson Tennant (see osmium, pp. 90–91) in the same platinum ore residue as osmium, iridium also gets its name from one of its properties, but this time a much nicer one! Taken from the name of the Greek goddess *Iris*, who was the goddess of the rainbow, iridium was so named since its compounds can take on many colours.

Natural allies and alloys

So closely related are osmium and iridium that osmiridium and iridosmine are examples of naturally occurring alloys of elements numbers 76 and 77. The names are straightforward enough, but a little misleading. Since they are naturally occurring, not only can the actual makeup of the alloys vary slightly from source to source, they usually also include other platinum group elements (see pp. 72–73) as part of their composition. As with most alloys, the combination of elements enhances the properties that either pure element would bring, and their superior strength and corrosion resistance is put to use in the nibs of expensive fountain pens. For the same reasons, as well as for its super-high melting point, iridium is also found in premium spark plugs; plugs made with iridium tips can outlast conventional plugs by thousands of engine miles.

◀ *The use of iridium in premium quality spark plugs has served to bring the metal to the attention of the general public, and helped position it as a somewhat exotic material.*

The International Prototype Kilogram, used as the standard for the metric SI unit of mass, was once pure platinum but now has iridium added.

Setting a standard

The International Prototype Kilogram, or IPK, is a cylindrical chunk of metal that defines the standard mass of one kilogram. The 39mm high and 39mm wide (1 1/2 in x 1 1/2 in) cylinder is kept at the International Bureau of Weight and Measures just outside Paris. The IPK, along with multiple copies, which are used for periodic verification and for practical purposes of calibration in other countries around the world, is made from a platinum and iridium alloy, the latter metal making up 10 percent of the object's mass. The original standard kilogram was pure platinum but iridium was added to enhance the hardness of the IPK. All of that may soon prove irrelevant, though, since the IPK is the final remaining artifact that defines such a standard, the others having been replaced by physical constants like the metre (see krypton, pp. 212–13). Interestingly, at one point in the past, another physical object, this time a metal bar also made from platinum and iridium, defined the standard length of one metre.

How high can you go?

When, in 2014, Chinese scientists managed to prepare an ion with the formula $[IrO_4]^+$, in the process they created a transition element with the oxidation state +9. A total of nine electrons had been removed from the metal, a feat never before achieved. This eclipsed the previous highest oxidation of +8, exhibited by osmium. In June 2016, scientists made predictions about oxidation states going one further to +10, in the platinum ion, PtO_4^{2+}.

Iridium's oxidation states

Oxidation state	Example
−3	$[Ir(CO)_3]^{3-}$
−2	unknown
−1	$[Ir(CO)_3(P[C_6H_5]_3)]^-$
0	$Ir_4(CO)_{12}$
+1	$Ir(CO)Cl(P[C_6H_5]_3)_2$
+2	$IrCl_2$
+3	$Ir_4(CO)Cl(H)_2(P[C_6H_5]_3)_2$
+4	$IrTe_2$
+5	$Ir(mesityl)_3O$
+6	IrF_6
+7	$[(\eta^2-O_2)IrO_2]^+$
+8	IrO_4
+9	IrO_4^+

Pt Platinum

Chemical symbol	Pt
Atomic number	78
Atomic mass	195.08
Boiling point	3825 °C (6917 °F)
Melting point	1768.4 °C (3215.12 °F)

⊛ *Like silver, most platinum jewellery is less than 100 percent pure. The metal's inertness and exclusivity make it a popular choice for wedding and engagement rings.*

As far as the precious metals go, platinum sits at the top, beating gold and silver hands down in most hierarchies. Consider, for example, the platinum disk awarded to US recording artists that sell one million copies of an album, compared to the mere 500,000 required for gold; silver doesn't even register on the scale. Where silver does enter the platinum equation is via the name: platinum is derived from the Spanish *platina*, meaning 'little silver'.

Pricey

Platinum's usefulness and position in the pecking order relates to its super-resistance to reactions with just about anything. As a silvery-white metal it has found favour as a popular choice for jewellery, in particular wedding rings, and platinum jewellery benefits from the fact that oxidation tends not to occur. Even though, like gold, one can find platinum free in nature,

it is not particularly widespread, being only the seventy-fifth most abundant element in the earth's crust. It is also reasonably difficult to extract and work with (it was often fused with arsenic to make it more workable), and coupled with a high demand, these properties make platinum routinely one of the most expensive metals in the world. As such, one might think that historically, platinum would have been a popular choice in the manufacture of coins. One notable example is the production of Russian rubles in the two decades prior to 1846. Around 1819, significant amounts of the metal were discovered in the Ural goldfields around the city of Ekaterinburg. This led to the minting of over one million coins. These coins have become collectors' items, fetching, in some cases, tens of thousands of dollars.

◀ *This platinum medal of 1826 shows Tsar Nicolas I of Russia. The use of platinum in Russia reached a peak in the early part of the nineteenth century.*

Platinosis and anti-cancer drugs

Although it sounds a little unlikely, platinosis – an allergic reaction to platinum salts – is indeed a real medical condition. It usually manifests itself via irritation of the upper respiratory system, and it is thought of as an occupational condition brought on by chronic exposure to platinum-based compounds. On a much more positive note, since the late 1970s, several platinum-based drugs have been used as anti-cancer medicines with great success. Developed after an accidental discovery, cisplatin (IUPAC name cis-diamminedichloridoplatinum(II), and with the chemical formula $[PtCl_2(NH_3)_2]$) inhibits cell division, and has been used as an incredibly successful anticancer drug. Like many drugs of its type, it is not without side effects, such as potential kidney damage, vomiting, and nerve problems, but it has nevertheless proven to be very effective, in particular, in the fight against testicular cancer.

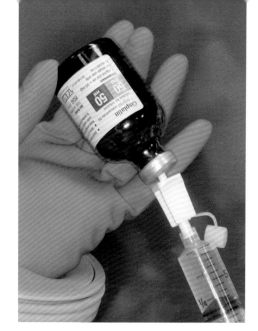

(▲) *Cisplatin is a platinum-based chemotherapy drug used in the treatment of many cancers, as it can help to arrest the growth of tumours.*

More catalysts, more alloys, more prizes

As we have seen earlier, when used as an alloy (see iridium, pp. 92–93), and as a catalyst (see rhenium, pp. 88–89, and rhodium, pp. 74–75), platinum exhibits many typical transition metal traits. In fact, the Nobel Prize in Chemistry in 2007 was awarded to Gerhard Ertl (b. 1936) for his work on 'chemical processes on solid surfaces'. That work included the action of platinum in the catalytic converter in turning the unwanted carbon monoxide in the exhaust gases of automobiles into the less poisonous, but still not entirely harmless, carbon dioxide.

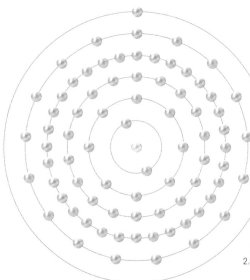

Electron configuration:
2.8.18.32.17.1

Au Gold

Chemical symbol	Au
Atomic number	79
Atomic mass	196.97
Boiling point	2856 °C (5173 °F)
Melting point	1064.18 °C (1947.52 °F)

Gold is one of the most iconic elements, a symbol of opulence and wealth (despite the fact that a number of elements are more costly and rarer). Its property of being relatively inert – and therefore able to resist corrosion – contributes to its ornamental appeal, and also means that gold has an important role in electronic applications where excellent, long-lasting electrical contact is crucial.

Gold has an important role in the history of chemistry, if for no other reason than that it partly drove the search for the philosopher's stone. Alchemists, as the pioneering chemists, had gold at the centre of their thoughts as they sought methods to convert base metals such as lead into the more valuable and prestigious ones. Many of those efforts laid the groundwork for what we know now as modern, quantitative and highly analytical chemistry, and gold was the enticing element.

A coveted element

As one of the coinage metals of group 11, gold sits vertically below copper and silver on the periodic table. Producing coins from gold makes sense, since there is a certain intrinsic value to element number 79; however, even as a relatively rare (it is the seventy-third most abundant in the earth's crust) and relatively expensive metal, there are several others that beat it in both categories. So what is it about gold that makes it so irresistible? It is probably due to its unique colour and its tremendous ability to resist corrosion over time, and hence maintain its distinctive shimmer. In fact, as it attracted the gaze of the earliest civilisations, that shine is what led gold to become

◀ *The search for the philosopher's stone and the quest for gold drove the alchemists, and, it can be argued, gave birth to much of modern chemistry in the process.*

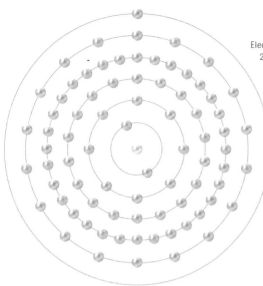

Electron configuration:
2.8.18.32.18.1

Nanomedicine

In 2012, scientists reported some success in treating prostate cancer with the use of gold-198 nanoparticles. The beta particles emitted from gold-198 have a range of approximately 1cm (3/8 in), so gold atoms inserted inside a tumour could attack the offending cells without going on to damage other nearby healthy cells. With a half-life of just under three days, the isotope is also a relatively easy one to manage.

one of the first known elements. Because of its appearance, and the fact that it is relatively soft and one of the easiest metals to work, around 75 percent of all of the gold produced is used in the manufacture of jewellery. Gold's ductility and malleability means that it can be hammered into ultra-thin sheets as gold foil.

Mining for gold in electronics

Gold's resistance to corrosion is not only an aesthetic attribute. In situations where it is absolutely vital for the conductivity of an electronic device to be maintained over time, gold is a popular choice for the contacts. In fact, the extensive use of gold in electronic devices has driven some people to attempt to recover it from discarded phones, cameras and laptops. The process is tedious and hazardous, and is likely to yield some very humble amounts of gold, but that hasn't put people off. In theory, several hundred pounds' worth of gold could be extracted from nothing more than a pile of electronic junk.

⊙ *Gold plays a role as a conductor in electronics, and there are significant amounts of the valuable metal in the tons of electrical goods that are discarded each year.*

Hg Mercury

Chemical symbol	Hg
Atomic number	80
Atomic mass	200.59
Boiling point	356.73 °C (674.11 °F)
Melting point	356.73 °C (−37.89 °F)

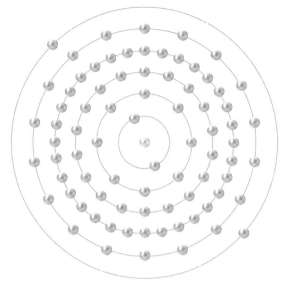

Electron configuration:
2.8.18.32.18.2

The adjective *mercurial* of course has its origins in Roman mythology and the messenger of the gods, Mercury. However, anyone who has seen his namesake element escape the confines of an old-fashioned thermometer and skate across the floor will recognise how appropriate it is that the metal, too, has come to be associated with all things erratic and changeable.

Ancient origins

The details of mercury's discovery as an element are lost in the mists of time, but knowledge of its source is well documented. Mercury's main ore, cinnabar, was known to ancient civilisations across the world as long ago as several thousand years BCE. Coveted for its brilliant scarlet colour, the rock – which is formed of the compound mercury(II) sulfide – was used to produce the red pigment known as vermilion.

Despite its glorious origins, mercury has a bit of an image problem in the modern world. A known toxin, mercury is associated with a wide range of health hazards. Whether it is connected with the poisoning of the developing foetus, or damage to the nervous, digestive and immune systems, it has caused sufficient concern to create a global initiative intended to reduce its buildup in the environment: the Minamata Convention on Mercury. One of the things addressed by the convention is the bioaccumulation of methylmercury in fish. As the organometallic ion $[CH_3Hg]^+$, naturally occurring mercury in water can be concentrated in organisms

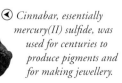

◀ *Cinnabar, essentially mercury(II) sulfide, was used for centuries to produce pigments and for making jewellery.*

and can ascend the food chain. When it reaches fish, not only is it many hundreds of times more concentrated than mercury found in the original environment, it is poised to enter the human food chain.

Millinery and madness

The Minamata Convention is named after the Japanese city of the same name where, in the late 1950s, an array of horribly debilitating symptoms came to light among the local population. Those symptoms included insanity, paralysis and ultimately death, and they were traced to pollution released from a chemical factory in the local area, which had been poisoning the local water supply with mercury for decades. Talking of insanity, the commonly used phrase 'as mad as a hatter' has its origins in the use of the nefarious heavy metal. In the nineteenth century, milliners used mercury to smooth out animal pelts in a process called 'carroting', where mercury(II) nitrate helped to mat the fine animal hairs together. Many hat makers developed 'hatter's shakes' – a condition that caused them to tremble – and other abnormal neurological conditions. So, after all the doom and gloom, are there any items on the positive side of the ledger? Well, to be honest, not a great deal. Mercury has been used in various products that reach the consumer, such as batteries and electrical components, but because of all the potential dangers, these uses are continuing

⊙ The legendary liquid metal also known as quicksilver has proved to be a fascinating element for centuries.

to decline. Now, mercury is used largely in industrial settings as a catalyst, for example, in the production of vinyl chloride monomer (VCM), a precursor to the more familiar polyvinyl chloride (PVC). However, even here, Minamata is having an effect. One specific part of the treaty requires all new VCM plants to be mercury-free by 2017, and five years later the goal is to eradicate it in this context completely.

⊙ Milliners used mercury(II) nitrate to smooth out animal pelts for fur hats. The health hazards for the hat-makers were considerable.

Post-transition metals

Also known as the 'poor' metals, these seven elements are certainly metallic in nature; they just aren't very good at being metals! Characterised by their relatively low melting and boiling points, poor strength and brittleness, their utility is often found in their use in alloys. When mixed with other, 'better' metals, properties that might otherwise be considered shortcomings can be utilised to manipulate the density, melting point and strength of composite materials.

On the following pages:

Al	Aluminium	Tl	Thallium
Ga	Gallium	Pb	Lead
In	Indium	Bi	Bismuth
Sn	Tin		

1 H																	2 He
3 Li	4 Be											5 B	6 C	7 N	8 O	9 F	10 Ne
11 Na	12 Mg											13 Al	14 Si	15 P	16 S	17 Cl	18 Ar
19 K	20 Ca	21 Sc	22 Ti	23 V	24 Cr	25 Mn	26 Fe	27 Co	28 Ni	29 Cu	30 Zn	31 Ga	32 Ge	33 As	34 Se	35 Br	36 Kr
37 Rb	38 Sr	39 Y	40 Zr	41 Nb	42 Mo	43 Tc	44 Ru	45 Rh	46 Pd	47 Ag	48 Cd	49 In	50 Sn	51 Sb	52 Te	53 I	54 Xe
55 Cs	56 Ba	57–71	72 Hf	73 Ta	74 W	75 Re	76 Os	77 Ir	78 Pt	79 Au	80 Hg	81 Tl	82 Pb	83 Bi	84 Po	85 At	86 Rn
87 Fr	88 Ra	89–103	104 Rf	105 Db	106 Sg	107 Bh	108 Hs	109 Mt	110 Ds	111 Rg	112 Cn	113 Nh	114 Fl	115 Mc	116 Lv	117 Ts	118 Og

	57 La	58 Ce	59 Pr	60 Nd	61 Pm	62 Sm	63 Eu	64 Gd	65 Tb	66 Dy	67 Ho	68 Er	69 Tm	70 Yb	71 Lu
	89 Ac	90 Th	91 Pa	92 U	93 Np	94 Pu	95 Am	96 Cm	97 Bk	98 Cf	99 Es	100 Fm	101 Md	102 No	103 Lr

The aluminium alloy magnalium can be used in hand-held sparklers to produce bright white sparks.

In the mix

Classic examples of transition metal alloys include solder (tin and lead), bronze (copper and tin) and a whole host of aluminium alloys with evocative names that sometimes give away their composition, like magnalium (magnesium and aluminium), and are sometimes less obvious, like duralumin, which contains copper, magnesium and manganese, along with aluminium.

Periodic trends

Found on the periodic table in groups 13, 14 and 15, the metals are known as 'post-transition' for a fairly obvious reason: they appear after the transition metals in groups 4 to 12. I have chosen aluminium, gallium, indium, tin, thallium, lead and bismuth to be part of this collection, although different sources sometimes include other elements, including those from groups 11 and 12 to the left, and 16 and 17 to the right. The recent addition to the periodic table of elements 112 to 117 also provokes interesting conversations about their ultimate classification.

The position of the post-transition metals on the periodic table is worth careful consideration. With the archetypal metals to their left, and the metalloids (whose metallic properties are increasingly diluted) to their right, the post-transition metals serve as a useful reminder of how periodic trends in the table work. With 'no-doubt' metals on the far left of the table, and 'no-doubt' non-metals on the far right, as one traverses the table from left to right, one can expect a gradual metamorphosis of metallic to non-metallic behaviour. The gap between the two extremes is bridged first by the poor metals, and then by the metalloids – which, perhaps by the same token, might collectively be renamed the 'poor non-metals'.

Lead, together with tin, forms part of the important alloy solder, which is used for joining electrical components.

Al Aluminium

Chemical symbol	Al
Atomic number	13
Atomic mass	26.982
Boiling point	2519 °C (4566 °F)
Melting point	660.32 °C (1220.58 °F)

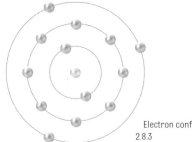

Electron configuration:
2.8.3

Aluminium (aluminum in American English) may now be ubiquitous, and relatively cheap, but this wasn't always the case. For the first few decades since its discovery, aluminium was regarded as one of the most precious of all metals. It was treated as such, and revered, until a young Frenchman and a young American perfected a way to produce it for a sensible price.

From rare to omnipresent

In 1870, the *Boston Journal of Chemistry* noted the following: 'Aluminium does not at present seem likely to become the familiar household metal that writers ten years ago predicted it would.' This was in reference to the fact that, despite somewhat successful efforts by the French chemist Henri Sainte-Claire Deville (1818–81) to reduce the cost of manufacturing element number 13, it was still financially out of reach. The story goes that another Frenchman, Paul Héroult (1863–1914), and an American, Charles Hall (1863–1914), each independently read a book Deville had written on aluminium production, and each was inspired to seek a more commercially viable way to obtain the light but strong metal. Each man worked independently

⊙ *The most common ore of aluminium is the mineral bauxite, essentially aluminium hydroxide, which is electrolysed to produce the metal.*

◄ *Aluminium metal has many applications thanks to its strength coupled with its low density. For example, when filled, this milk churn remains light enough to carry.*

on perfecting an electrolytic process, and each came to almost exactly the same conclusion, via almost exactly the same process, at almost exactly the same time. The so-called Hall-Héroult process revolutionised the production of aluminium, and the metal became the uber-popular material it is today.

Aluminium is the most abundant metal in the earth's crust, and the third most abundant element overall. Like the other poor metals, on its own aluminium is quite weak and relatively soft. However, as an alloy, its low density becomes a huge asset. The metal is extraordinarily workable, meaning that it can be drawn into wires (ductility), shaped (malleability), smelted and cast, as well as rolled into sheets and even produced in powder form. This versatility means that aluminium

⊛ A very workable metal, aluminium can be machined into extremely thin sheets before being fabricated.

has found uses in a huge number of areas, ranging from construction (where an oxide layer allows it to resist corrosion), to household cookware (it has high heat conductivity), to the manufacture of food cans. It also plays a vital role in the aerospace and aircraft industry, where its high strength-to-weight ratio makes it a hugely important component of a large number of alloys. Along with other important metals, notably titanium (see pp. 44–45), aluminium is alloyed to produce metals that have superior composite qualities to the individual metals alone.

Ga Gallium

Chemical symbol	Ga
Atomic number	31
Atomic mass	69.723
Boiling point	2204 °C (3999 °F)
Melting point	29.76 °C (85.57 °F)

Gallium's claim to fame is that it is *almost* a liquid at room temperature. The fact that it melts at around 30 °C (86 °F) means that unlike mercury, whose unique appearance as a liquid metal at room temperature is obvious, gallium usually has the appearance of a solid, shiny metal. Even body heat, however, will be enough to convert it to a pool of silver-coloured liquid.

⊙ *Unusually, for a metal, elemental gallium expands when it solidifies, meaning that, like water, its solid form will float in its own liquid.*

Predicting periodicity

Gallium is not only a fascinating element in terms of its properties, but also in terms of its history. Mendeleev had predicted the existence of gallium long before it was actually found or named. As with eka-boron, eka-caesium, and eka-silicon, Mendeleev had come to the conclusion that his nascent arrangement of elements had to allow for the ultimate insertion of some as yet undiscovered elements. These would account for some apparent gaps in the periodic pattern he had derived. Mendeleev predicted that an element he called eka-aluminium would have properties that, among others, included an atomic mass of 68, a density of 6.0 g/cm^3 and a low melting point.

When, in 1875, Frenchman Paul-Émile (François) Lecoq de Boisbaudran (1838–1912) discovered a new element, he found that its properties were astonishingly similar to Mendeleev's eka-aluminium – with one exception. Lecoq de Boisbaudran found the density of the material he had discovered to be much lower than Mendeleev's prediction. This turned out to be an experimental error on the part of the Frenchman, and he ultimately recorded a new value much closer to Mendeleev's number. As we shall also see with germanium (pp. 122–23), such was the accuracy associated with Mendeleev's predictions that the discovery of gallium helped to solidify the whole idea of the periodic table and its patterns beyond any reasonable doubt.

The disappearing spoon

The title of Sam Kean's *New York Times* bestselling book about chemistry, *The Disappearing Spoon* (2010), is a homage to gallium and the tricks it can play. In the book, not only does Kean outline the spat that occurred between Mendeleev and Lecoq de Boisbaudran in great detail, he also describes a practical joke involving gallium, whereby a spoon made of the metal is plunged into a hot cup of tea. Of course the spoon

Electron configuration:
2.8.18.3

disintegrates completely, leaving the would-be stirrer horrified!

In addition to its low melting point, gallium has a huge range of temperatures where it remains liquid – the largest liquid range of all the elements and comparable only to tin. This property led to gallium being used in (now antiquated) quartz thermometers, where the temperature range that could be monitored was between 600 and 1,500 °C (1,112–2,732 °F).

⊙ *Gallium's famously low melting point is often highlighted by the fact that the warmth from one's hand is sufficient to melt the metal.*

In Indium

Chemical symbol	In
Atomic number	49
Atomic mass	114.82
Boiling point	2072 °C (3762 °F)
Melting point	156.60 °C (313.88 °F)

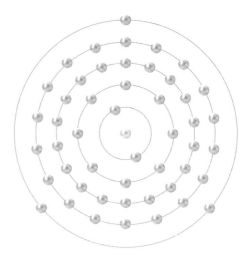

Electron configuration:
2.8.18.18.3

Indium was discovered in 1863 by the German pair Ferdinand Reich (1799–1882) and Hieronymus Theodor Richter (1824–98). While working at the Freiberg School of Mines, Reich noticed something odd about a yellow solid he had produced when experimenting with a mineral form of zinc. When the new material was interrogated it revealed a hitherto unknown blue-purple-coloured line in its spectrum. They christened the new metal after the Latin *indicium*, meaning 'violet/indigo', in recognition of the coloured line they had observed.

Lead-like

Indium resembles many of the elements around it on the periodic table, not only in group 13 (Ga and Ti) as one would expect, but also diagonally down to its right, where we find lead. Like lead, indium is a very soft metal, with a value of 1.2 on the Mohs scale (see p. 127) of hardness compared to lead's 1.5. It has a high density (7.31 g/cm^3 versus 11.34 g/cm^3 for lead) and it melts at a relatively low temperature of 157 °C (315 °F) compared to lead's 327 °C (621 °F).

An ingot of pure indium. In appearance, indium is somewhat unremarkable and could easily be mistaken for any number of other, similar elements.

 *Solar cells are often coated with thin films of indium alloys, such as copper indium gallium selenide, which is is an excellent absorber of sunlight.*

Metal mimic

Indium is commonly found in a number of naturally occurring zinc compounds. This curiosity is linked to the relative sizes of the Zn^{2+} ion and the In^{3+} ion, indium's most common oxidation state (the charge on the ion). The zinc ion has a radius of 88 pm (pm stands for Picometre and is equal to 1×10^{-12} metres), and that of the indium ion is 94 pm. As with thallium (pp. 110–11) and potassium (pp. 18–19), this kind of similarity can lead to one ion mimicking another, and explains why indium is so often found associated with ores that contain Zn^{2+}.

The liquid mirror

As a modern material, indium finds few uses, but like so many of the metals in this collection, alloys are important. Those alloys are similar to many others of the post-transition metals inasmuch as that they often have very low melting points. Mixed with its fellow group 13 family member and fellow low-melting point metal gallium, indium (along with a little tin) can produce an alloy that is liquid at room temperature. The resultant alloy, galinstan, is a shiny, silver-coloured liquid that can be applied to glass in order to create a mirrored surface. Another of indium's alloys, indium tin oxide, is used to produce highly conductive, transparent coatings for touch screens, flatscreen displays, and solar cells.

Sn Tin

Chemical symbol	Sn
Atomic number	50
Atomic mass	118.71
Boiling point	2602 °C (4716 °F)
Melting point	231.93 °C (449.47 °F)

Tin is one of the ancient elements. Arguably, its greatest contribution to civilisation is as a component of one of the most historically important alloys ever known: bronze. As early civilisations moved from using stone for implements and weapons, to metals, tin was mixed with copper to produce the alloy. Bronze was so critical to the development of early man that a whole period of civilisation was named after it.

The 'tin' can

The Latin name for tin was *stannum*, hence the somewhat confusing chemical symbol for tin, Sn. Just like lead, the element below it in the periodic table, tin is relatively soft with a low melting point. It is a silvery-white metal, and is resistant to corrosion in a similar way to aluminium: they both form a protective oxide layer on the surface of the metal. This property was utilised in one of its largest applications, the 'tin can'. Even when first invented in the early part of the nineteenth century, the tin can was not made exclusively from tin; in fact, it contained very little tin at all. Most cans were made from steel, with a thin coating of tin applied to prevent rusting. Tin's resistance to corrosion meant that even the acidic nature of many foods would not damage the can, and goods could be kept in cans and preserved for long periods. Modern 'tin' cans are often made

⊙ *These Bronze Age implements represent an important milestone in human deveopment: the move from using tools made of stone to those made of metal.*

from aluminium, which offers similar resistance to corrosion but is lighter and cheaper.

Tin's use in canning is also partly due to the fact that in many compounds tin is non-toxic. This is especially true of inorganic compounds, where tin combines with non-metals. One such example is tin(II) fluoride, which is used as a fluoride delivery agent in toothpastes. The same benign nature cannot be said of many organic compounds of tin. In these compounds, rather than combining with non-metals, tin combines with carbon atoms in the form of alkyl groups such as methyl (CH_3) and ethyl (C_2H_5). These have been used as fungicides, although their use has been banned in some instances over concerns regarding pollution.

Tin has a curious tendency to disintegrate into a powder at extremely cold temperatures, and this property perpetuated a poorly founded myth about the demise of the Napoleonic army in Russia in 1812. (The 2003 science book by Penny Le Couteur and Jay Burreson, *Napoleon's Buttons*, takes its title from this myth.) The story as originally told suggests that the extreme cold of the Russian winter caused the tin buttons on the uniforms of the Napoleonic

 'Tin' cans have evolved in terms of their composition and construction over the years, but they were never made purely from tin metal.

army to disintegrate, and hence led to their defeat. This story has been refuted, but a similar story has been recounted about the British expedition led to the Antarctic by Robert Falcon Scott (1868–1912). In this case, it seems likely that the tin solder that held the party's kerosene rations *did* disintegrate, causing them to lose vital fuel and contributing to their deaths in March 1912.

Electron configuration: 2.8.18.18.4

Tl Thallium

Chemical symbol	Tl
Atomic number	81
Atomic mass	204.38
Boiling point	1473 °C (2683 °F)
Melting point	304 °C (579 °F)

Perhaps one of the most controversial of all elements, not only was thallium's discovery subject to much debate, it also has a more sinister reputation as an element of murder! Sitting horizontally on the periodic table between a couple of almost as nefarious metals, mercury and lead, thallium is a soft, silver-white metal that typically forms two ions, Tl^+ and Tl^{3+}. The former of these is the source of many of the element's problems.

⊙ Sir William Crookes was a pioneer in the use of spectroscopy for the identification of elements. He also founded and edited Chemical News, *an important magazine that reported advances in chemistry.*

Controversy from birth

In 1861, Englishman William Crookes (1832–1919) observed the distinctive green line in the spectrum of thallium, which led to his claiming priority for its discovery. Things, though, were not quite so simple, largely due to the almost simultaneous work done by Frenchman Claude-Auguste Lamy (1820–78). Lamy also observed the spectral lines that Crookes had seen, and he too laid claim to the discovery. Lamy's claim was cemented by the fact that he also managed to isolate the pure element in 1862. It was not until Crookes became a Fellow of the Royal Society in 1863, and pulled rank, that the controversy was settled: Crookes was given the recognition.

Heavy stuff

Even considering its place among a nasty array of heavy metals that can do all kinds of damage to human health, thallium can be considered a particularly offensive element. For a long time it was used as a rodent

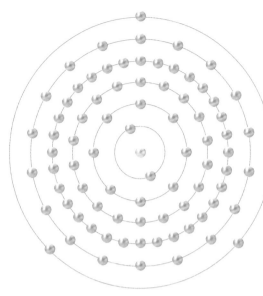

Electron configuration:
2.8.18.32.18.3

Murderous mimic

Although thallium is renowned for causing victims to lose their hair, that is far from being the element's most unpleasant effect. Its dastardly nature lies in two properties of the Tl^+ ion: it has the same charge (+1) as, and is a similar physical size to, the potassium ion, K^+. This means it has the ability to impersonate potassium ions in many biological situations – and that presents a huge problem. While potassium ions are crucial to the correct function and well-being of human cells, thallium ions can have quite the opposite effect. One of thallium's unpleasant tendencies is for it to interfere with proteins that contain sulfur atoms. The reactions between these species can result in the disruption of protein structures in the body and of the nervous system. That's bad enough, but coupled with the frightening ease with which it is absorbed through the skin, thallium is truly an element not to be trifled with.

poison. Making such a potentially deadly element available as an everyday consumer product is seldom a good idea, and after a combination of accidental poisonings and treacherous murders (both in fiction and in real life), it was banned from sale in the United States in 1972. Unfortunately, that did not quash the murderous intentions of some people, including Tianle Li. Li worked as a chemist at a lab where she had access to thallium, and over a period of approximately three months, between November 2010 and January 2011, she used the deadly element to fatally poison her husband. She was sentenced to life in prison in 2013.

⊙ *Elemental thallium held under an argon atmosphere. Thallium is a soft, malleable, silver-coloured metal that discolours rapidly in air.*

Pb Lead

Chemical symbol	Pb
Atomic number	82
Atomic mass	207.2
Boiling point	1749 °C (3180 °F)
Melting point	327.46 °C (621.43 °F)

Known for its softness, malleability, and high density, lead is one of the more familiar metallic chemical elements. But while it may be familiar, it is not well thought of in the twenty-first century. Lead has become increasingly frowned upon as its poisonous nature has become better understood and increasingly publicised. The need to remove lead from paints and petrol, and to prevent it from tainting the water supply, has harmed the element's public image.

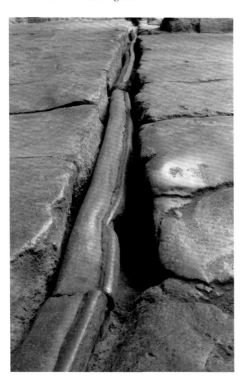

⊙ Lead was used to make water pipes for plumbing for thousands of years. This lead pipe was used to deliver water to Roman baths in Bath, England.

So civilised

As an element known to ancient civilisations, lead has no particular discoverer. Its use dates back several thousand years, with extensive applications in a whole host of early everyday items, such as water pipes, pottery glazes and lead cooking pots. Lead water pipes were used extensively by the ancient Romans because of the element's durability and malleability, and plumbing was still being made of lead well into the twentieth century. (As lead's toxic nature was increasingly understood, lead pipes were phased out in new construction, and replaced by plastic or copper.) The combination of its use as cookware, and its being at the heart of the water supply infrastructure, is thought by some to have been a contributing factor in the decline of the Roman Empire, in particular by depressing the birth rate. Even so, the Roman influence on the history of lead remains indelible, with the symbol for element number 82 derived from the Latin for lead, *plumbum.*

◀ *Galena is the natural mineral form of lead(II) sulfide and is an important ore of lead.*

batteries, especially those used in cars, where, combined with sulfuric acid, it makes a rechargeable cell. It may also be used as a shield to protect humans from harmful radiation, in particular via the 'lead apron' used at the dentist's office when X-rays are taken.

The toxic protector?

Like several post-transition metals, lead has been used in a number of historically important alloys. Solder (tin and lead) is used to join metal pipes, and pewter (tin, copper, antimony, bismuth and lead) has been used to make decorative tableware. However, the concern regarding the use of lead has haunted even these applications, and solder and pewter are much less extensively used than they once were. Lead does still find application in

Dead lead?

Lead's popularity was initially driven by its relative abundance in the earth's crust, and the fact that it can be so easily smelted and worked with. However, its heyday was almost certainly several thousand years ago, and its fate now seems sealed; the assault on the use of lead keeps coming. One of the latest stories to hit the headlines was the water crisis in Flint, Michigan, USA, where in 2014 problems with the treatment of drinking water meant that thousands of residents were exposed to extremely high levels of the metal. The short-term health effects were relatively minor ones such as skin rashes, but the long-term consequences are harder to predict. Lead's role in hindering and damaging brain development in young people is one particular black mark that is difficult to shake off, and only time will tell how the children of Flint will fare in the long run.

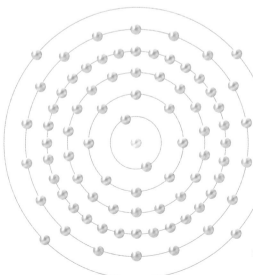

Electron configuration:
2.8.18.32.18.4

Bi Bismuth

Chemical symbol	Bi
Atomic number	83
Atomic mass	208.98
Boiling point	1564 °C (2847 °F)
Melting point	271.40 °C (520.52 °F)

As a neighbour of lead, bismuth has spent most of its history in the shadow of the element to its left, not least because it was confused with lead for much of its early existence. Bismuth resembles lead in many of its properties, and when the science of chemical analysis was in its infancy, the confusion with lead was inevitable. Known now as a distinct element, bismuth is still a little obscure, finding very few common applications.

Bismuth has an extraordinarily complex history that started to emerge in the late fifteenth century, mainly in Germany. However, it wasn't until 1753, when French chemist Claude François Geoffroy (1729–53) published his observations in *Mémoires de l'académie française*, that bismuth became recognised as a distinct element in its own right.

Wood's metal

Bismuth's comparisons to other elements do not end with lead. Much of its chemistry is similar to other elements in the group 15 family, notably antimony and arsenic. Bismuth is also used in alloys – the quintessential application for so many of the poor metals. The bismuth alloy of primary importance is known as Wood's metal, an alloy that was developed by Barnabas Wood (1819‑75), an American dentist. His alloy, made from about 50 percent bismuth with varying amounts of lead, tin and cadmium, had a melting point of only 70 °C (158 °F). The applications for an alloy with such a low melting point may not necessarily be all that obvious – surely such a property would be a potential hindrance to its usefulness? However, this tendency to melt at a low temperature has two particular applications that have helped to make the world a safer place. As a component of fire sprinklers, Wood's metal is used as a plug that seals a water pipe. As a fire burns, the temperature around the plug increases, eventually melting the metal plug,

◀ *Bismuth crystals can produce some incredible colours, as the iridescent oxide layers on their surface catch light in different ways.*

The relatively low melting point of Wood's metal, an alloy of bismuth, allows plugs in sprinkler systems to melt, releasing water from the extinguishers.

Going from the most mundane self-medication to some of the most extreme chemistry ever conducted – nuclear fusion – makes for an interesting juxtaposition, but bismuth has played a role in both. As a target nucleus, bismuth-209 was bombarded with iron-58 atoms and the result was a new element. In 1982, a single, short-lived atom of element number 109, meitnerium-266, was produced in this way by Peter Armbruster (b. 1931) and Gottfried Münzenberg (b. 1940) in Germany.

and as a result, releasing water. In a similar application, gas canisters can be fitted with valves made of Wood's metal so that, in a fire situation, the canister will open, releasing the gas inside and thus reducing the risk of a cylinder exploding. Unfortunately, with both lead and cadmium present, the concerns over the potential toxicity of Wood's metal has limited more extensive modern use.

Heartburn and nuclear fusion

A more familiar application of bismuth is that of one of its compounds, bismuth subsalicylate. Under the commercial name Pepto-Bismol, the bright-pink liquid is sold as an over-the-counter medicine used to treat mild stomach ailments such as diarrhoea, indigestion and heartburn. Its medicinal qualities are perhaps surprising given bismuth's proximity in the periodic table to a couple of deadly elements, lead and polonium.

Electron configuration:
2.8.18.32.18.5

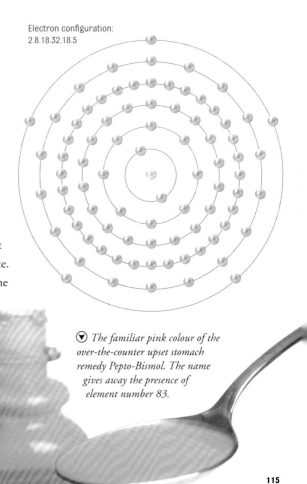

The familiar pink colour of the over-the-counter upset stomach remedy Pepto-Bismol. The name gives away the presence of element number 83.

115

Metalloids

The metalloids are an eclectic bunch. Not only does this ragtag collection of elements exhibit chemical and physical behaviours that cut across the boundaries between metals and non-metals, they are also found scattered between groups 13 and 17 of the periodic table. Consequently, they have varying numbers of electrons in their valence shells, and since valence electrons drive chemical behaviour, these elements exhibit a wide variety of chemical properties.

On the following pages:

B   **Boron**

Si **Silicon**

Ge **Germanium**

As **Arsenic**

Sb **Antimony**

Te **Tellurium**

Po **Polonium**

1 H																	2 He
3 Li	4 Be											5 B	6 C	7 N	8 O	9 F	10 Ne
11 Na	12 Mg											13 Al	14 Si	15 P	16 S	17 Cl	18 Ar
19 K	20 Ca	21 Sc	22 Ti	23 V	24 Cr	25 Mn	26 Fe	27 Co	28 Ni	29 Cu	30 Zn	31 Ga	32 Ge	33 As	34 Se	35 Br	36 Kr
37 Rb	38 Sr	39 Y	40 Zr	41 Nb	42 Mo	43 Tc	44 Ru	45 Rh	46 Pd	47 Ag	48 Cd	49 In	50 Sn	51 Sb	52 Te	53 I	54 Xe
55 Cs	56 Ba	57–71	72 Hf	73 Ta	74 W	75 Re	76 Os	77 Ir	78 Pt	79 Au	80 Hg	81 Tl	82 Pb	83 Bi	84 Po	85 At	86 Rn
87 Fr	88 Ra	89–103	104 Rf	105 Db	106 Sg	107 Bh	108 Hs	109 Mt	110 Ds	111 Rg	112 Cn	113 Nh	114 Fl	115 Mc	116 Lv	117 Ts	118 Og

		57 La	58 Ce	59 Pr	60 Nd	61 Pm	62 Sm	63 Eu	64 Gd	65 Tb	66 Dy	67 Ho	68 Er	69 Tm	70 Yb	71 Lu
		89 Ac	90 Th	91 Pa	92 U	93 Np	94 Pu	95 Am	96 Cm	97 Bk	98 Cf	99 Es	100 Fm	101 Md	102 No	103 Lr

What are they, anyway?

Some of the elements that are usually included in this assemblage are made up of relatively small, light atoms, whereas others have very heavy atoms. The size and mass variation adds to the complexity of their different behaviours, and settling on any universal description for the metalloids as a whole is virtually impossible. Muddying the water even further is the fact that over time, the term 'metalloid' itself has had a number of different meanings. The modern meaning (that of exhibiting both the properties of metals and non-metals) is still somewhat ill defined. Adding to the confusion is the use of the similar term 'semimetal', plus the various failed attempts by IUPAC to unify the definition.

It is probably not surprising, then, given the difficult history associated with even the word itself, that chemists cannot completely agree on which elements should be considered metalloids. Without a specific definition, the classification of metalloid has spanned a considerable number of elements. Elements that one might normally consider to be firmly in the realm

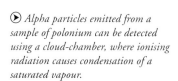

◀ *The absolute classification of metalloids like antimony is not easy. Historically, different criteria have been applied to their identification.*

of metals – such as zinc, tin, chromium and lead – and those that are commonly considered non-metals without much dispute – like nitrogen, sulfur and phosphorous – have, at one time or another, been classified as metalloids. In modern chemistry the elements that are most commonly thought of as metalloids are boron, silicon, germanium, arsenic, antimony and tellurium, with polonium and astatine sometimes joining those six. In this book, we will consider the most common half-dozen plus polonium to be 'our' metalloids.

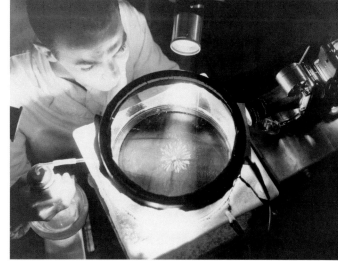

▶ *Alpha particles emitted from a sample of polonium can be detected using a cloud-chamber, where ionising radiation causes condensation of a saturated vapour.*

B Boron

Chemical symbol	B
Atomic number	5
Atomic mass	10.81
Boiling point	4000 °C (7232 °F)
Melting point	2075 °C (3767 °F)

Boron is not easy to obtain as the pure element. There is not a whole lot of it in the earth's crust, and what little there is, is either tied up in compounds or tends to be contaminated with carbon. For those reasons boron is better known for its appearance in its various compounds, rather than as a distinct, freestanding element.

Borax

Important compounds of boron are many and various. They also have a confusing array of names that are sometimes used somewhat interchangeably, which can muddy the water even further. Borax, borates and boric acid all contain boron, but are subtly different in terms of their composition and use. Borax is perhaps the most familiar compound that includes element number 5, and is a particular type of borate (a compound where boron is combined with oxygen to produce a negative ion, such as $B_2O_5^{4-}$). Borax actually refers to the sodium salt $Na_2B_4O_7$, although it too has several different formulae depending on how much water is associated with the compound.

⊙ *Borax mines are characterised by being highly visible. The mining is 'open-pit', and as such, the borax can often be seen at the surface.*

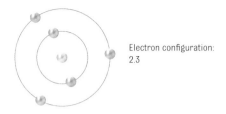

Electron configuration: 2.3

Borax has found use as a historical cosmetic, a modern-day laundry detergent, a flux in the manufacture of steel to lower the melting point of the alloy and to allow it to be worked more easily, a food additive (as E285 it is used as a preservative) and a water softener.

What a bore

Although borax had been known for centuries, as an element boron only came into its own in the early part of the nineteenth century. In 1808 it was first isolated almost simultaneously by the French duo of Louis Joseph Gay-Lussac (1778–1850) and Louis Jacques Thénard (1777–1857), and by English chemical giant Humphry Davy. The French and the English had different ideas about the name of the new element, with the French favouring the somewhat unfortunate moniker of *bore*. In the end, the name was coined by Davy from a combination of the 'bor' part of borax, and the ending of the related non-metal carbon.

Nuclear applications

Elemental boron finds an important application in nuclear reactors. One of the fundamental tenets of producing nuclear energy is that when a nuclear fission reaction takes place, neutrons are one of the by-products. These neutrons go on to create other fission events that in turn produce even

Ⓐ *Borax has been part of a wide variety of household cleaning and laundry products over the years, such as 'Borax Extract of Soap'.*

more neutrons. This sets up a chain reaction. In order to control such reactions, and to generate nuclear energy efficiently and safely, there needs to be a way of absorbing some of the neutrons that are produced and therefore controlling the reaction. Boron-10's nuclear structure (with an odd number of neutrons) makes it an excellent absorber of slow neutrons, so it is often used in control rods in reactors.

Si Silicon

Chemical symbol	Si
Atomic number	14
Atomic mass	28.085
Boiling point	3265 °C (5909 °F)
Melting point	1414 °C (2577 °F)

Silicon is synonymous with the American high-tech industries. The connection stems from the name the element lends to the Santa Clara Valley south of San Francisco. Silicon's reach, however, extends far beyond the West Coast of the United States – literally! As the second most abundant of all the elements, its sheer presence on earth is massive.

Silicon beach

Silicon is omnipresent on earth and has always been known to people, but has certainly not always been recognised as an element. The most obvious example of silicon's presence is sand, which is essentially silicon dioxide, SiO_2. As if to drive home the fact, sand is also known as 'silica'. When the number of oxygen atoms combined with silicon varies from just two, for example, in the negative ion SiO_4^{4-}, then the word 'silicate' is used. In fact, more generically, silicate can even be used to describe anions of silicon that do not contain oxygen, such as hexafluorosilicate, SiF_6^{2-}.

Although he was ultimately proved wrong, silica was one of the 'elements' included in Antoine Lavoisier's original 1789 list, in the seminal work *Traité Élémentaire de Chimie*. Moving forward a couple of decades, Humphry Davy knew that silica was not an element, but while he successfully extracted metals with electrolysis in the first few years of the nineteenth century, he failed in his attempts to do the same with silica. It was not until 1824 that Jöns Jacob Berzelius finally managed to extract element number 14, and he named it 'silicium'. Unfortunately, the *-ium* ending is usually associated with metallic elements, so when it was realised that silicon was a non-metal, the name was changed to silicon in order to match the similar non-metal elements carbon and boron.

◀ *Silicon at the beach? Yes, that's silicon in the form of its oxide, which forms hard, solid sand crystals.*

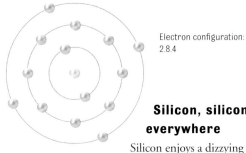

Electron configuration:
2.8.4

Silicon, silicon everywhere

Silicon enjoys a dizzying array of applications in many different forms and compounds. Sand is an essential component of glass; and silicones (compounds of silicon, oxygen and organic carbon chains) are extensively used in applications such as silicon rubber and silicone oil lubricants, and in plastics. One familiar use is in silicone sealants in the plumbing industry. Silicones have excellent water-repellent properties and can be moulded to fit into cracks and crevices to seal the system.

Of course, in the late twentieth and early twenty-first centuries, silicon's major impact has been in the role of a semiconductor in the electronics industry – but not as a lone element. Starting in its pure form, silicon is

The water resistance of many silicon-based products make them popular choices for kitchen and bathroom sealants.

'doped' by the addition of tiny amounts of other elements. Silicon is found in group 14 of the periodic table, and therefore possesses four valence electrons. By replacing small numbers of silicon atoms with elements from the adjacent groups 13 or 15 (gallium or boron from 13, and arsenic or antimony from 15), the conductivity of silicon is increased. The group 13 elements introduce a 'hole' (three valence electrons where there were once four), and the group 15 elements an extra electron (five valence electrons where there were once four), and each adjustment allows for electrons to move more freely in the material.

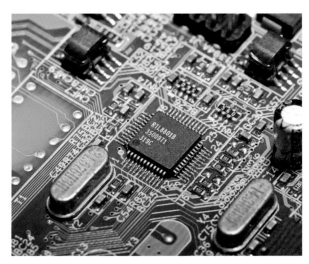

Perhaps the most well-known application of silicon is in the microprocessor industry, where its use as a semiconductor is ubiquitous.

Ge Germanium

Chemical symbol	Ge
Atomic number	32
Atomic mass	72.630
Boiling point	2833 °C (5108 °F)
Melting point	938.25 °C (1720.85 °F)

The most Germanic of all the elements – it is named after the Latin for Germany, *Germania* – element number 32 is one of the most historically important. Germanium has many of the properties of silicon, and much of its chemistry is related to element number 14. However, germanium is significantly less abundant than silicon in the earth's crust; in fact, of the five naturally occurring elements in group 14, it is the rarest.

(A) *Although it's a metalloid, germanium can take on a super-shiny lustre that could easily be mistaken for that of a classic metal.*

The key to the table

Germanium's history is of particular interest largely because of the role it played in the development of the periodic table. Mendeleev had predicted the existence of several 'as yet undiscovered' elements, which, he said, would ultimately fit into some gaps in the element sequence that he had proposed. One of the missing was a group 14 element that Mendeleev believed would have properties that would place it in his table between silicon and tin. He called it eka-silicon. When, in 1886, Clemens A. Winkler (1838–1904) finally discovered germanium in a new mineral unearthed in a German mine, the properties

(◄) *German chemist Clemens A. Winkler isolated germanium from the mineral argyrodite, a mixed sulfide containing significant amounts of both germanium and silver.*

that Mendeleev had predicted for the missing element were found to be incredibly close to the actual properties of germanium. Mendeleev had predicted a relative atomic mass of 72 (the value for germanium was found to be 72.32) and a specific gravity of 5.5 (the value for germanium was 5.47). The accuracy of the predictions made by Mendeleev about eka-silicon helped to firmly cement the Russian's reputation and the role of the periodic table as a cornerstone of chemical theory. Mendeleev had other successes in predicting properties of elements that would be found later, notably, eka-boron (scandium), eka-aluminium (gallium) and eka-manganese (technetium).

Doped for the better

Like silicon, its closest neighbour in group 14, germanium is a semiconductor that can be doped with group 13 and group 15 elements to increase its conductivity (see p. 121). In compounds, specifically as the dioxide, it finds other uses that are related to the refractive index of the composite material. GeO_2 has a relatively high refractive index (the physical property that causes

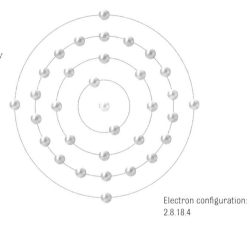

Electron configuration: 2.8.18.4

light to 'bend' as it passes from air into a transparent substance such as water or glass). The addition of germanium dioxide to glass can create a material that is able to collect light from a large field of view, and is therefore useful in wide-angle camera lenses.

▶ *The optical properties of germanium oxide allow it to be used in wide-angle camera lenses, where its low optical dispersion makes it an ideal material.*

As Arsenic

Chemical symbol	As
Atomic number	33
Atomic mass	74.922
Boiling point	subl. 616 °C (1140.80 °F)
Melting point	817 °C (1503 °F) (at 28 atm)

Arsenic is an element with somewhat of an image problem. As with other elements, such as sulfur, there are many forms of arsenic, this time characterised by their colours (yellow, grey and black), but whatever the form, arsenic tends to mean only one thing – poison! The nefarious images of murderous serial killers that it conjures up, even before one knows anything about it, ensure that as an element, its reputation is firmly established.

Arsenic is another of the ancient elements. Its discovery is sometimes attributed to Albertus Magnus (c. 1200–80), a thirteenth-century friar and bishop (and later a Catholic Saint), but the precise history of its discovery is shrouded in doubt.

▶ *German physician Paul Ehrlich developed a cure for syphilis when he perfected the arsenic-based medicine known as Salvarsan.*

Kill or cure?

Arsenic's deadly reputation is a shame, because it also has a fascinating history of use as a medicine, advertised to cure a plethora of ailments and diseases. Most of the claims by the early doctors and charlatans of the seventeenth and eighteenth centuries were pure quackery, but one Nobel Prize-winning physician, the German Paul Ehrlich (1854–1915), developed what turned out to be a very important, 'real' medicine based on arsenic.

At the turn of the nineteenth century the sexually transmitted disease syphilis was a serious social problem. In 1909 Ehrlich tested a huge array of arsenic-containing compounds on diseased rabbits, and the one that cured them came to be known commercially as Salvarsan. It was a little risky to administer, and one had to be careful not to poison the patient, but it did work. Ultimately, penicillin proved to be a better bet.

Dyeing and dying

One early and popular use of arsenic compounds was in dyes and paints, in particular yellows and greens. Modern-day usage of arsenic is perhaps most important in the doping of semiconductors used in modern electronics. Here, the As atoms of group 15 replace the Si atoms of group 14 in order to increase conductivity. This substitution creates what is known as an n-type conductor, where 'n' stands for negative. A group 15 element has five valence electrons, whereas a group 14 element has only four. The extra negatively charged electron creates an increase in conductivity, and with it an increase in utility, of the pure silicon.

Highly toxic to humans, arsenic and its various compounds cause a variety of ailments – notably, serious problems with the skin and lungs – and can quickly cause death. Many criminals chose arsenic as a poison in the nineteenth century, not least of all because it was difficult to detect. That all

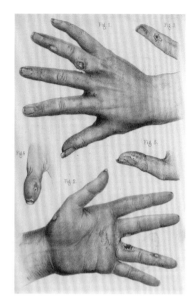

◀ *This lithograph, titled 'Accidents caused by the use of green arsenic dyes', was published in a French periodical in 1859.*

changed in 1836 when the British chemist James Marsh (1794–1846) developed a test to detect minute amounts of arsenic. The test converts the arsenic oxide that is present in poisoning cases to arsine, AsH_3, and the subsequent heating of this compound creates a distinctive deposit of elemental arsenic known as a black arsenic mirror. Marsh's test was first used in the field of forensic science in France in 1840, when it was employed to solve the mariticide of Charles Lafarge.

Electron configuration:
2.8.18.5

▶ *Arsenic has a number of allotropic forms, including yellow, black and grey, with the grey form being the most common of all.*

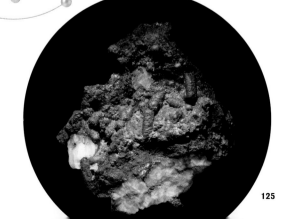

Sb Antimony

Chemical symbol	Sb
Atomic number	51
Atomic mass	121.76
Boiling point	1587 °C (2889 °F)
Melting point	630.63 °C (1167.13 °F)

Antimony's classification as a metalloid is well earned. As a metal, it is similar to lead, and throughout history it has often been mistaken for element 82, but it also has properties that are far less metallic. For example, it exists as a number of different allotropic forms in a similar way to classic non-metals carbon and sulfur.

Antimony eyeliner

As one of the ancient elements known to mankind, there is no recorded, specific discoverer of antimony. The metalloid is found to occur naturally in a mineral with the formula Sb_2S_3, known as stibnite, hence its somewhat unlikely chemical symbol, Sb. Artifacts made from the pure element, and that date back 5,000 years, have been found. The ancient Egyptians and earlier civilisations knew of antimony, and one of the earliest uses of the element was as a primitive cosmetic known as kohl. Kohl has a fascinating history all of its own, and is still used extensively in the twenty-first century, with many people in Africa and Asia still using it as an eyeliner. It is used by both men and women, and mothers have applied it to the eyes of their babies and young children for centuries, especially in India. Kohl has a number of different forms and varying chemical content depending on where and by what tradition it is made, but blue kohl is known to contain large amounts of antimony in the form of stibnite. Claims and counterclaims relating to both

⊙ Perhaps the earliest cosmetic, kohl's use as an eyeliner goes back to Ancient Egypt.

⊙ A double wooden kohl tube from Egypt, dated 100 BCE–400 CE. It would have been used to store ground stibnite, a mineral containing antimony, to be used as kohl.

⚫ *From early Egypt to modern-day Asia, kohl continues to be used in the manner that it has been for centuries, despite controversy over its safety.*

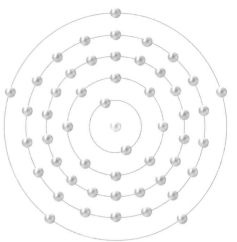

Electron configuration:
2.8.18.18.5

the health benefits (protecting the eyes from disease in developing countries) and the health risks (exposing children to large amounts of potentially harmful lead and antimony compounds) rage on, but in many parts of the world, tradition and belief mean that the practice of applying kohl continues to this day.

Babbitt metals

In commercial applications, antimony finds use in alloys, and it lends interesting properties to lead alloys in particular. Pure lead is especially soft. The Mohs scale is used to define how hard a substance is, and it uses a number scale of 0–10, where lower numbers are associated with softer materials. Lead's Mohs value of 1.5 makes it one of the softest metals known, and although on the grand scale antimony is not what one might call 'hard' (with a Mohs scale value of 3.0), it certainly adds hardness to any mixture it makes with lead. In the nineteenth century, and for much of history since, a whole family of other alloys that included antimony

has played a crucial role in engineering. Babbitt metals, invented by American goldsmith Isaac Babbitt (1799–1862), are an array of alloys of varying composition. In Babbitt metals, tin, lead, copper and arsenic are mixed in varying percentages with antimony. The unique crystalline structure of the resulting alloys means that the materials have an extremely low coefficient of friction, so they are used extensively as bearing surfaces where moving metal components come into contact with one another.

⚫ *Like several of the metalloids, antimony has a tendency to appear like a metal when it is in its elemental form.*

Te Tellurium

Chemical symbol	Te
Atomic number	52
Atomic mass	127.60
Boiling point	988 °C (1810 °F)
Melting point	449.51 °C (841.12 °F)

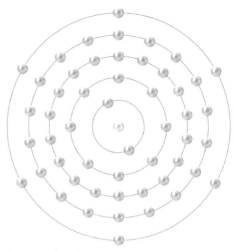

Electron configuration:
2.8.18.18.6

As a member of group 16 of the periodic table, tellurium shares some similarities with its non-metal cousin sulfur, in particular its association with some wholly unpleasant odours. 'Tellurium breath' is a condition in which the body converts the smallest traces of tellurium into the organic compound dimethyl telluride, $(CH_3)_2Te$, producing a foul, garlic-like odour. Anyone exposed to tellurium could be detected from some distance away!

Tellurium has an unusual connection to the precious metal gold. After a lot of confusion surrounding tellurium's discovery, in 1783 Franz-Joseph Müller von Reichenstein (1740/42–1825) finally identified tellurium in a mineral that he had been studying for some time. As the chief surveyor of mining in Transylvania,

Müller von Reichenstein's job involved the analysis of previously unidentified ores as they came to light. At first the ore in question was thought to contain bismuth and antimony, but it was later discovered that the mineral was gold telluride, which is itself somewhat unusual. Gold is renowned for its lustre, which is due to its being such an unreactive metal. As a relatively inert element, it forms very few naturally occurring compounds, but the original ore of tellurium is one of them.

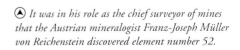

⊙ *It was in his role as the chief surveyor of mines that the Austrian mineralogist Franz-Joseph Müller von Reichenstein discovered element number 52.*

Out of order

Tellurium, much like fellow metalloid germanium, also had a role to play in the history of the periodic table. Mendeleev's early renditions of the table proved problematic in terms of the ordering of the elements. When Mendeleev arranged the elements in order of their increasing masses, he found that iodine would need to come before tellurium. However, the observed chemical properties of the two elements clearly demanded that the sequence be reversed, with tellurium preceding iodine. It was not until the early twentieth century, when Henry Moseley

◀ Elemental tellurium in its crystalline form takes on a silvery, metallic lustre. At room temperature it is a solid, with a melting point just under 450 °C (842 °F).

championed the idea of ordering elements by their atomic numbers (the number of protons in the nucleus), that the problem was resolved and tellurium could take its rightful place before iodine.

The same but different

Today, tellurium has similar uses to other metalloids. Like antimony, for example, tellurium has found use in alloys of lead in order to harden and strengthen the material, and like germanium, it has found use in glass manufacturing. And tellurium's similarities with other elements do not end there. The process of vulcanization involves sulfur being added to rubber in order to create cross-links within the rubber that increase the utility of the material. Like its group 16 cousin, tellurium has also found a role in vulcanization, where its addition can both harden rubber and make it easier to work with.

◀ Vulcanization of rubber in the US circa 1946–50. Tellurium aids the vulcanization process, much like its fellow group-16 element sulfur.

Po Polonium

Chemical symbol	Po
Atomic number	84
Atomic mass	209 (longest-living isotope)
Boiling point	962 °C (1764 °F)
Melting point	254 °C (489 °F)

One of the most politically charged elements on the periodic table, polonium has attracted more than its fair share of controversy. It was named by its discoverer, Marie Curie, after her native Poland, which was then occupied by foreign forces. Curie's hope was that her homeland's plight might be brought to worldwide attention, and that independence might follow. Just over 100 years after its discovery, polonium became infamous for its role in a twenty-first-century spy story.

The Curies

Polonium is found in uranium ores, but it is a very rare element and was therefore difficult to find and isolate. Marie Curie and her husband, Pierre, extracted the first sample of the element from pitchblende, a uranium-rich ore, in 1898. Their interest was aroused as the pitchblende that they were studying was emitting an enormous amount of radioactivity, which could not be attributed to the uranium alone. Polonium is brutally radioactive as an alpha particle emitter, and is extremely dangerous. Sadly, it is cited as the element that caused Marie Curie's daughter Irène Joliot-Curie's (1897–1956) death from leukaemia in 1956, following her exposure to a broken vial of the element ten years earlier.

◀ *Marie and Pierre Curie discovered polonium in pitchblende, the primary ore of uranium.*

▼ *Polonium is cited as the element that led to the death of Marie Curie's daughter, Irène Joliot-Curie (left below).*

Polonium-210

Polonium is a soft, silvery-grey element that physically resembles its horizontal neighbour to the left on the periodic table, bismuth, but is chemically similar to its vertical group 16 neighbour tellurium. It forms a large number of isotopes, but by far the most interesting and infamous is polonium-210.

When Alexander Litvinenko fled to London in 2000, the former Russian secret service officer was already in hot water. He had publicly accused the state of ordering assassinations for political gain, and he had been arrested and incarcerated in his native country on more than one occasion. His defection to the UK would have been frowned upon under any circumstances, but when he began to work with the British intelligence services, and then wrote two books that outlined further

Russian dissident Alexander Litvinenko was assassinated in London in 2006, by being poisoned with radioactive polonium-210.

accusations against the Russian hierarchy, some might say that his fate was sealed. After eating out at a London restaurant in November 2006, Litvinenko suddenly fell ill and was hospitalised. Three weeks later he was dead. It was determined that Litvinenko had been exposed to an unusually large dose of polonium-210, and that he had died as a result of the radiation sickness caused by the deadly isotope. Polonium-210 has a radioactive half-life of 138 days, and decays by emitting positively charged alpha particles. Alpha particles can be stopped in air or by a piece of paper, but their ability to badly damage tissues and organs if inhaled or swallowed is what makes polonium-210 so dangerous.

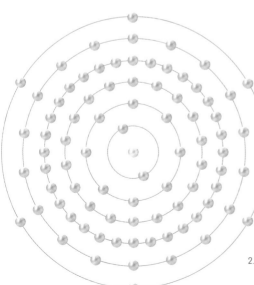

Electron configuration:
2.8.18.32.18.6

Lanthanoids

As in many other examples of our grouping of elements, the lanthanoids – previously also known as the lanthanides (see the actinoids, pp. 164–77) – have their own complicated history of elemental inclusion and exclusion, with, in this case, the addition of a terribly misleading collective name. Sometimes referred to as the rare earth elements, that moniker creates problems of its own that only serve to muddy the water further.

On the following pages:

La Lanthanum   Sm Samarium   Ho Holmium

Ce Cerium   Eu Europium   Er Erbium

Pr Praseodymium   Gd Gadolinium   Tm Thulium

Nd Neodymium   Tb Terbium   Yb Ytterbium

Pm Promethium   Dy Dysprosium   Lu Lutetium

1 H																	2 He
3 Li	4 Be											5 B	6 C	7 N	8 O	9 F	10 Ne
11 Na	12 Mg											13 Al	14 Si	15 P	16 S	17 Cl	18 Ar
19 K	20 Ca	21 Sc	22 Ti	23 V	24 Cr	25 Mn	26 Fe	27 Co	28 Ni	29 Cu	30 Zn	31 Ga	32 Ge	33 As	34 Se	35 Br	36 Kr
37 Rb	38 Sr	39 Y	40 Zr	41 Nb	42 Mo	43 Tc	44 Ru	45 Rh	46 Pd	47 Ag	48 Cd	49 In	50 Sn	51 Sb	52 Te	53 I	54 Xe
55 Cs	56 Ba	57–71	72 Hf	73 Ta	74 W	75 Re	76 Os	77 Ir	78 Pt	79 Au	80 Hg	81 Tl	82 Pb	83 Bi	84 Po	85 At	86 Rn
87 Fr	88 Ra	89–103	104 Rf	105 Db	106 Sg	107 Bh	108 Hs	109 Mt	110 Ds	111 Rg	112 Cn	113 Nh	114 Fl	115 Mc	116 Lv	117 Ts	118 Og

57 La	58 Ce	59 Pr	60 Nd	61 Pm	62 Sm	63 Eu	64 Gd	65 Tb	66 Dy	67 Ho	68 Er	69 Tm	70 Yb	71 Lu
89 Ac	90 Th	91 Pa	92 U	93 Np	94 Pu	95 Am	96 Cm	97 Bk	98 Cf	99 Es	100 Fm	101 Md	102 No	103 Lr

First, considering the term 'rare earth' is used to describe them, it would seem reasonable to think that these elements are, well, rare. Not so. In fact, some of the elements are relatively abundant in the earth's crust compared to many others found on the periodic table. Second, because of their extreme chemical similarity (much of their chemistry is based upon the +3 oxidation state indicated by the generic Ln^{3+}), they proved to be an extraordinarily difficult group of elements to separate from one another and to identify as distinct. Their history is littered with mistaken identity, false claims and general confusion, including the mildly ridiculous story of two of them, terbium and erbium, being mixed up, to the point where terbium became erbium, and erbium became terbium! Finally, when the term 'rare earths' is used, it automatically includes the transition metals scandium and yttrium within the lanthanoids. See what I mean about confusion?

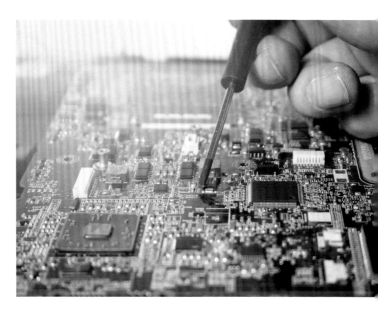

⬆ *The ubiquitous presence of so many lanthanoid metals in a vast array of personal electronics, such as mobile phones and laptops, means that they are valuable resources, but with demand increasing, their sustainability is under question.*

Supply and demand

The rare earths/lanthanoids have been thrown into the spotlight in recent years because of the astonishing growth in the personal electronics industry. Many of the elements in this collection are used in the production of mobile phones, laptops and all manner of other small electronic devices; as such, their sustainability is of increasing concern. Matters are further complicated by geopolitics, with China playing a major role as both a supplier and a user of lanthanoids. One solution is to seek alternative materials that can replace elements whose supply might ultimately be threatened, but not all of the elements can be easily substituted. Among the lanthanoids, europium, dysprosium, thulium and ytterbium are particularly difficult to replace with alternatives. Given that the technology is unlikely to slow down anytime soon, it's likely that interest and intrigue will continue to surround many of these elements well into the future.

La Lanthanum

Chemical symbol	La
Atomic number	57
Atomic mass	138.91
Boiling point	3464 °C (6267 °F)
Melting point	918 °C (1688 °F)

Lanthanum is the first, the lightest, and one of the more abundant of the lanthanoids, and of course, the element that the series is named after. As mentioned previously, the lanthanoids are a nightmare to get at because not only do they all tend to cluster together in their ores, but their chemistry is similar. In that respect, the name of element number 57 seems particularly appropriate.

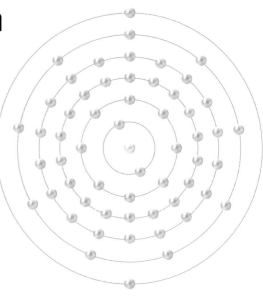

Electron configuration:
2.8.18.18.9.2

When Carl Gustaf Mosander (1797–1858) discovered lanthanum in a sample of cerium nitrate in 1839, he turned to the problems associated with isolating the rare earth elements from one another as inspiration for element number 57's name. He named the new element lanthanum, after the Greek *lanthanein*, meaning 'to lie hidden'.

◀ *The Swede Carl Gustaf Mosander was a prolific chemist, not only discovering lanthanum, but also erbium and terbium among the lanthanoids.*

Mishmash metal

German can be an extraordinarily literal language, with compound words producing combinations that leave even non-native speakers without much doubt as to their meaning. OK, but what's that got to do with lanthanum? Well, take the word *mischmetal*, meaning 'mixed metal' in English. This refers to a combination of lanthanoids of varying specific composition, but with significant amounts of lanthanum; there are also varying amounts of praseodymium and neodymium present, along with some iron. These metals have a fantastic ability to create sparks, and are used as flints in cigarette lighters.

⊛ *A solid sample of the soft, silvery-white metal that is the first of the lanthanoids, and the element that gave the series its name.*

From problematic to no problem

Usually, the similarity between all of the lanthanoids is a huge problem, but in the case of mischmetals, what is often a pain can become a boon. Since all of the elements act in such similar ways, the same effect can be achieved no matter what the actual combination of elements used, meaning that their composition need not be precise. That's a good thing, since it means that one need not go about the painstaking process of separating them.

Dating rocks

In a similar way that its fellow lanthanoid samarium (pp. 144–45) is used, an isotope of lanthanum, La-138, can be utilised in the radioisotope dating of very (and I mean very) old rocks. La-138 has a half-life of 1.05×10^{11} years, and one of its decay products is an isotope of barium, Ba-138. By measuring the relative amounts of these isotopes present in a lump of ancient rock, geologists can make decent estimates of the age of some extremely old geological forms. The process is known as 'LaBa dating', from the symbols of elements 57 and 56.

Bending light and cleaning up

Lanthanum and several of its compounds have a myriad of other, smaller applications, one of the better-known being the role of the oxide, La_2O_3, in the manufacture of speciality glass. Lanthanum oxide increases the refractive index of the glass so it can be used for camera lenses. Lanthanum chloride is another interesting compound, which is used in swimming pool and aquarium maintenance. By adding soluble $LaCl_3$, phosphates in the water can be precipitated out, helping to control the growth of green algae, which thrives where phosphates are present.

Ce Cerium

Chemical symbol	Ce
Atomic number	58
Atomic mass	140.12
Boiling point	3443 °C (6229 °F)
Melting point	799 °C (1470.20 °F)

Cerium is the most abundant of all the rare earth elements, and in fact, as the twenty-fifth most abundant of all the elements in the earth's crust, it is actually anything but 'rare'. Cerium is also (or at least can be) one of the more spectacular elements. A lump of cerium metal is described as being pyrophoric, meaning that when it is struck or scratched, it will emit a shower of sparks.

(A) *Ferrocerium produces sparks when struck against a rough material, making it a useful material for fire-starters and cigarette lighters.*

In the first few years of the nineteenth century, interest in celestial bodies was aroused by the observation in 1801 of a new asteroid, named Ceres. A couple of years later, a new chemical element was found. In 1803, Wilhelm Hisinger (1766–1852) – with the help of Jöns Jacob Berzelius – discovered element number 58, and the new lanthanoid was named after the recently observed asteroid.

Burn, baby, burn

As mentioned under lanthanum (see pp. 134–35), cerium's ability to produce sparks means that it is used as a flint in mischmetals, and it can be combined (chiefly with iron) in an almost identical material called, appropriately, ferrocerium.

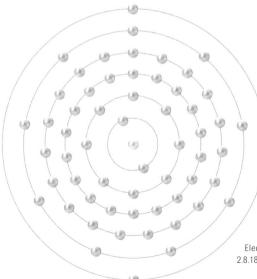

Electron configuration:
2.8.18.19.9.2

Strikers are commonplace in laboratory settings, where ferrocerium is used to create the spark for lighting burners.

Ferrocerium has been marketed under a number of different trade names as a fire-starter for camping enthusiasts. With just a hint of irony, cerium salts can also be used to treat burns in the compound cerium(III) nitrate, $Ce(NO_3)_3$. The nitrate salt is usually used in combination with a silver compound, silver sulfadiazine, where it is applied as a cream.

Replacing red, oxides and cheating

Another compound of cerium, this time an oxide, turns up in a couple of places. It is insoluble so can be added to water and then applied to glass, where it acts as a fine abrasive, polishing the glass in the preparation of specialist lenses. In some applications, cerium(IV) oxide has replaced the abrasive known as 'iron oxide rouge', also known as 'jeweller's rouge', a dark red compound used for a similar purpose. Cerium oxides are also employed in the catalytic converters mentioned under a number of other elements (see rhodium, pp. 74–75 and palladium pp. 76–77). As part of the cleaning process, cerium oxide helps to promote the oxidation of unburned hydrocarbons

to carbon dioxide and water, and carbon monoxide is converted to carbon dioxide. The compound also helps to collect NO_x gases in the process, in what is called a 'lean NO_x trap'. In this type of catalytic converter, oxides of cerium can be used to turn the potentially harmful NO_x gases into the relatively benign nitrate salts of the metal. This technology hit the news in 2015, when the German car manufacturer Volkswagen was caught up in an emissions cheating scandal. At home, the oxide can be used in self-cleaning ovens to do a similar job.

In another example of a red compound of one element being replaced by one containing cerium, cerium sulfide is being substituted for other, heavy-metal-based pigments that are either patently unsafe or environmentally unfriendly. One such example is the replacement of toxic cadmium compounds (see pp. 80–81) with a cerium-based compound known as 'pigment red 265'.

Iron oxide rouge, also known as jeweller's rouge, is used for polishing, but cerium has replaced its use in many instances.

Pr Praseodymium

Chemical symbol	Pr
Atomic number	59
Atomic mass	140.91
Boiling point	3520 °C (6368 °F)
Melting point	931 °C (1707.80 °F)

It's next to impossible to separate praseodymium and its periodic table neighbour and twin element, neodymium, from one another. On the other hand, one could say that the pair were actually separated at birth, and when you learn the meaning of the two names, things become even more intertwined. Praseodymium is taken from the Greek *prasinos didymos*, meaning 'green twin', and neodymium from *neos didymos*, meaning 'new twin'.

In keeping with what had at times seemed like a hopeless quest to separate the rare earths into their individual boxes on the periodic table, elements 59 and 60 came to illustrate that struggle better than most. In the first instance Mosander – the discoverer of lanthanum (pp. 134–35) – thought that he had discovered a new element mixed up in samples of the already known cerium and lanthanum. In what turned out to be an astonishing piece of serendipity, he called this new 'element' 'didymium', after the Greek word for 'twin'. He did so since he thought that the new element was so much like lanthanum. Even though it turned out that didymium was not an element at all, Mosander's choice of name could hardly have been more prophetic.

Separating the twins

It was not until spectroscopy came into its own that there was a decent chance of actually identifying many of the lanthanoids in any definitive way. Enter Carl Auer von Welsbach (1858–1929), a student of Robert Bunsen's, and hence well positioned to exploit his spectroscopy technique to aid with further element identifications. Not only did Auer von Welsbach perform many tedious separations of the lanthanoid ores, he also went on to confirm that didymium was in fact two elements – Mosander's original name could hardly

◀ *Carl Auer von Welsbach invented the gas mantle and several techniques related to separation and spectroscopy.*

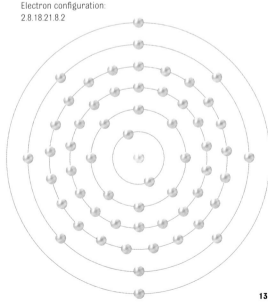

⊗ A hydrate sample of praseodymium(III) sulfate with eight water molecules associated with each formula unit of the salt.

⊗ A sample of an aqueous solution of praseodymium nitrate, viewed on a microscopic slide, and illuminated with polarised light.

have been a better one, but for a different reason than he had originally imagined! Named for the colour of its oxide, praseodymium (along with its 'twin', neodymium) was discovered in 1885.

Back together in glasses

After all of the aggravation of the discovery of elements 59 and 60, and the struggle to identify and separate them, it is more than a little ironic that one of the chief uses of praseodymium is back with neodymium in a mixture known as, of course, didymium – Mosander would have been delighted! When mixed together, the two lanthanoid elements are used to make the lenses of safety spectacles used by glassblowers. When mixed, the metals have a peculiar property. Their combination leads to a substance that allows the intense orange-yellow light that is

emitted when glass that contains sodium (see pp. 16–17) is heated to be completely filtered out, thus protecting the craftsman's eyes from damage. In a related use, when glass and ceramics need a little colour of their own, praseodymium can be added to give green and yellow hues.

Electron configuration:
2.8.18.21.8.2

Nd Neodymium

Chemical symbol	Nd
Atomic number	60
Atomic mass	144.24
Boiling point	3074 °C (5565 °F)
Melting point	1021 °C (1869.80 °F)

Despite the fact that, in many senses, elements 59 and 60 are almost totally entwined, neodymium has one reason to stand out on its own. Thanks to one single property, first discovered in the 1970s, neodymium might be the most well-known and most familiar of the all of the lanthanoids.

⊙ *Neodymium magnets are the strongest permanent magnets. They have many applications, including in computer disk drives and MRI machines.*

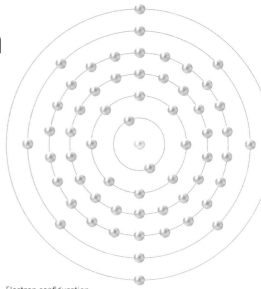

Electron configuration:
2.8.18.22.8.2

Magnetic madness

There are magnets, and then there are magnets. The combination of neodymium, iron and boron makes for some ferociously strong, permanent magnets. When combined in the correct ratio, $Nd_2Fe_{14}B$, the elements together create an ultra-strong magnetic field. This is partly due to the crystal structure of the compound that is formed, and partly due to the fact that neodymium has seven unpaired electrons in its electron configuration. Unpaired electrons create their own tiny magnetic fields, and when billions of atoms are lined up in a single direction, the accumulation of these tiny fields creates a very strong magnetic force. Recent research has suggested that neodymium magnets can be used to open magnetically sensitive ion-channels in the brain, resulting in the non-invasive tweaking of neurons, and

▶ *Neodymium magnets are sometimes marketed as 'executive' toys.*

Laser light

As we saw when we looked at praseodymium (pp. 138–39), neodymium has an important application in didymium glass, and it has a few other, quite specialised applications too. One is in the production of lasers. Here, neodymium is used as a doping agent, where it introduces a small impurity into a crystal that is then used to produce the laser. A couple of examples are its use with the YAG crystal (see yttrium, pp. 62–63), and with another yttrium compound, yttrium lithium fluoride, or YLF. These lasers have several applications, including in medicine, where they have been used for corrective eye surgery.

hence potentially helping with the treatment of neurological disorders. The neodymium magnets can act on specially modified proteins containing paramagnetic iron ions, and this allows calcium and sodium ions (see pp. 16–17) to flow, regulating many electrical functions in the body.

When used in more traditional ways, these magnets produce such extremely strong magnetic fields that they would be hazardous if one were to get between two of them. Most accidents connected with neodymium magnets involve children, because not only can the magnets prove fascinating to them, but they have been marketed as toys in some instances, a controversial move because of the danger they pose.

Do not eat!

The most common type of accident involves a child swallowing a pair of magnets. Once ingested, the super-strong magnets have a habit of rapidly finding one another, and violently snapping together. If that occurs when one magnet is in one part of the intestine or stomach, and the other magnet is in another part, then as the magnets collide they can pinch and perforate the small intestine, bowel or stomach wall. Obviously, that is incredibly dangerous, and at least one death has been reported, as have two other horrendously unpleasant incidents involving neodymium magnets: one involving a finger, and one involving a penis!

▼ *YAG lasers, whch are doped with neodymium, are used in medical and dental applications.*

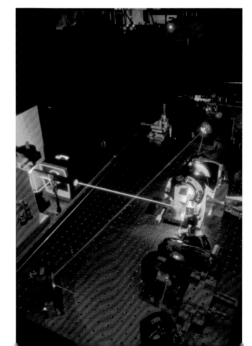

Pm Promethium

Chemical symbol	Pm
Atomic number	61
Atomic mass	145 (longest-living isotope)
Boiling point	3000 °C (5432 °F)
Melting point	1042 °C (1908 °F)

Promethium suffers from the same issues as technetium (see pp. 70–71) inasmuch as it has no stable isotopes and so is basically 'missing' from the earth's crust. Add to the mix the difficulty of separating one rare earth from another, and you have quite the conundrum. As a result, element number 61 was a tough one to find, and it was 1945 before its discovery was finally confirmed.

False starts

Of course, formal confirmation is one thing, but as we have seen with a number of other elements in this book, that didn't stop several people claiming – and naming – element number 61. Before it was named after the Greek Titan Prometheus, promethium had at least two other prominent names. In the mid-1920s two serious claims were made

on element 61. In the United States, a group of scientists at the University of Illinois thought that they had observed spectral lines that could be attributed to the missing lanthanoid. They were so sure that they went ahead and christened the element 'illinium', after their home state. All of that home-state pride proved misplaced, however, when it was pointed out that the lines in question could be attributed to a large amount of impurities in the sample. Home-based pride was also in evidence in the other claim for element number 61 that was made around the same time. Two Italian scientists working at the Royal University in Florence conducted similar research, and named their version of the element 'florentium'. The Italians claimed to have done their research prior to the Americans and said that they had kept their findings a secret. As such, they thought that they should be given priority. In the end, whose research came first didn't matter in the slightest, since their claim, like that of the Americans, was ultimately dismissed.

Ⓐ *Uraninite, or pitchblende, a uranium ore, in which most of the earth's naturally occurring promethium is found.*

Finally, in Tennessee

At least one more rejected name (cyclonium) went before the actual discovery of promethium in 1945 by a group at the Oak Ridge National Laboratory (ORNL) in Tennessee. They observed element number 61 in fission products at ORNL's Graphite Reactor. The labs at Oak Ridge have played a major role in a number of important nuclear experiments that have led to the confirmation of many of the heaviest known isotopes. The lab was a collaborator on the recent confirmed discoveries of elements 115 and 117, with the latter, tennessine, being named in honour of the work done in the state where Oak Ridge is located.

Beta uses

Unfortunately, as a relevant element in terms of its chemistry and applications, promethium barely registers. The fact that so little of it exists, and that there are no naturally occurring isotopes that are stable, means that what little is used needs to be obtained from other nuclear events. There are a couple of places where Pm-147 beta emission is put to use. Luminous paints have in the past contained the isotope (see radium, pp. 38–39), and it can be used as a thickness gauge, where concentrations of beta particles emitted can be used to determine the thickness of paper as it is manufactured.

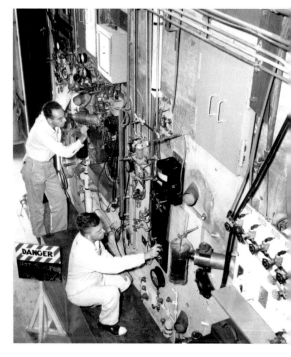

⊕ *The Oak Ridge National Laboratory graphite reactor in Oak Ridge, Tennessee, where element number 61 was first detected, in 1945.*

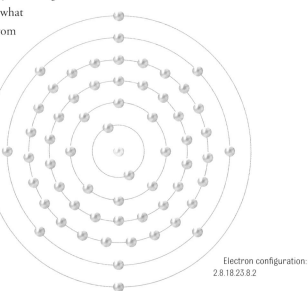

Electron configuration:
2.8.18.23.8.2

Sm Samarium

Chemical symbol	Sm
Atomic number	62
Atomic mass	150.36
Boiling point	1794 °C (3261.20 °F)
Melting point	1074 °C (1965.20 °F)

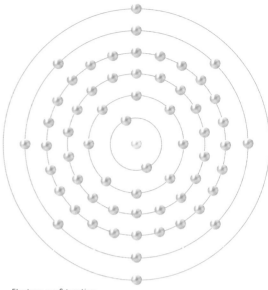

Electron configuration:
2.8.18.24.8.2

Depending on how one wants to define it, element number 62 could be described as the first element to be named after a living person. A shiny metal that reacts with oxygen, it is the second most abundant of the lanthanoids, being made up of a number of naturally occurring isotopes. Three of those isotopes have extraordinarily long half-lives, which has led to their use in a complicated dating technique called geochronology.

Samarium can be found in a number of rare earth ores, notably cerite, gadolinite, samarskite, monazite and bastnäsite. One of its isotopes, Sm-147, has an extraordinarily long half-life of 1.06×10^{11} years, and this is useful in dating rocks and other geological formations. Samarium-147 undergoes alpha decay to neodymium-142, and by measuring the amount of samarium and its daughter isotope present in any given sample, it is possible to estimate the age of material going back millions of years.

Eponymous elements?

In reality, samarium was actually named after the mineral that it was extracted from, samarskite. However, the German mineralogist Heinrich Rose (1795–1864) had, in turn, named samarskite after Vasili Samarsky-Bykhovets (1803–1870). Samarsky-Bykhovets was a high-ranking Russian mine official who had provided the original sample of the mineral for analysis, so whether the element is actually named after the Russian or the mineral is open to some debate. To get on more solid ground

A sample of the mineral samarskite, from which samarium is mined and takes its name.

in terms of elements named after living people, then one needs to look to element 106, seaborgium, and the newly minted oganesson, element 118. Seaborgium was named after the American nuclear chemist Glenn Seaborg, initially in 1994, and then formally by the IUPAC in 1997. It took that long simply because there had been several years of arguing between rival Russian and US nuclear groups over names that had to be mediated by the IUPAC. By the time 2016 came around and oganesson was proposed for element 118 in honour of the Russian nuclear physicist Yuri Oganessian, the IUPAC had a better handle on the whole naming process, and much less debate took place. Both of these men might have been preceded by Albert Einstein (1879–55) and Enrico Fermi (1901–54), who both died shortly before the elements named after them – numbers 99 and 100, respectively – were officially named.

Magnets and nuclear control

Samarium's uses are specialised and quite limited, but in an alloy with cobalt, the rare earth is used to make magnets that are resistant to demagnetization and also heat-resistant. It is certainly true that neodymium magnets (see pp. 140–41) are now more popular and more widely used because of their stronger magnetic properties and their relatively low cost, but the samarium–cobalt magnets are still preferred in applications where extreme heat may be encountered. The isotope Sm-149 is a good neutron absorber and is used in reactor control rods in a similar manner to boron (see pp. 118–19).

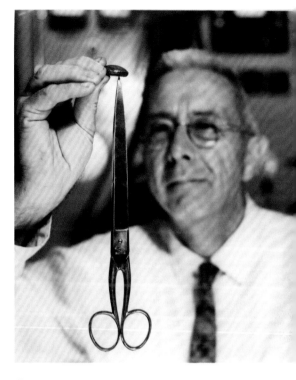

⬥ *A 1968 demonstration of the power of a magnet made from samarium and cobalt. It was then one of the most powerful small magnets ever made.*

▶ *Samarium and cobalt magnets are favoured over those made of neodymium in applications where the magnets need to stand up to extreme heat.*

Eu Europium

Chemical symbol	Eu
Atomic number	63
Atomic mass	151.96
Boiling point	1529 °C (2784 °F)
Melting point	822 °C (1511.60 °F)

Europium started life as an offshoot of its periodic table neighbour samarium. Europium had a few of the early spectroscopy gurus scratching their heads, with William Crookes and Paul-Émile Lecoq de Boisbaudran both noting some oddities in samarium samples. But it was left to Frenchman Eugène-Anatole Demarçay (1852–1903) to confirm europium, and isolate one of its salts in 1901. Why he called it europium, nobody seems quite sure.

Electron configuration:
2.8.18.25.8.2

Demarçay became an expert in spectroscopy, analysing experimental data to find new elements (in the case of europium), and helping in the confirmation of others like the Curies' radium (see pp. 38–39).

Red and blue

Europium first found utility through the phosphorescence of its compounds, notably as Eu^{3+} and Eu^{2+}. The latter is an example of a lanthanoid element finding favour in an oxidation state other than +3, a relatively unusual occurrence. Red colours are produced from phosphors that contain compounds with the higher-charged Eu^{3+} ion, such as Eu_2O_3, and europium in the 3+ state was used in old-fashioned televisions. Compounds of the lower oxidation state (+2) emit blue light and they are sometimes combined with the red europium(III) compounds and fellow lanthanoid terbium(III) compounds (green), in order to produce manufactured white light.

In 2015, work by scientists in Belgium was reported that involved the reclaiming of europium from discarded lightbulbs. In the experiments, Eu^{3+} ions from the phosphors were converted to Eu^{2+} ions by the absorption of light in a photochemical process. Then, by addition of sulfate ions, insoluble europium(II) sulfate can be precipitated out of solution and the metal recovered.

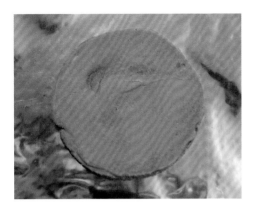

When the pure metal is exposed, a yellow film forms on the surface of europium metal.

the name! Another form of 'currency', the humble postage stamp, has also benefited from the chemistry of element number 63. Europium oxide has been incorporated into stamps to allow machines to recognise the glow given off by the europium ions, in order to establish the stamps' face value.

Take note, no forgery

Continuing europium's utility as an optical element, we find it in inks that are used to print banknotes. When viewing such currency under ultraviolet (UV) light, the europium ions absorb the UV light, and the electron movement that is caused by the transfer of such electromagnetic energy is responsible for the red light that is emitted. By incorporating the exotic inks into the notes, they become increasingly tricky to counterfeit convincingly. The specific chemical compositions of the compounds used as security inks are the subject of great secrecy (for obvious reasons), but there is plenty of speculation out there as to their content, including the idea that officials at the European Central Bank chose europium for use in their euro currency notes, over other, potentially equally suitable lanthanoids, just because they liked

Rays and rods

A number of patents have been filed for europium-doped polyethylene plastics, which have been shown to help enhance plant growth. These sheets, once again through the optical properties of europium, convert UV light present in natural sunlight to a light source that the plants can use in the photosynthesis process. Another good neutron absorber, europium also appears in some control rods for nuclear reactors.

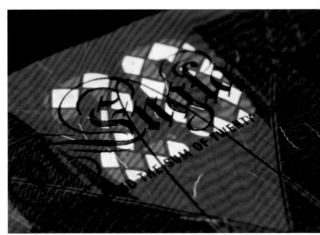

The use of inks containing europium has greatly helped in the fight against the counterfeiting of currency.

Gd Gadolinium

Chemical symbol	Gd
Atomic number	64
Atomic mass	157.25
Boiling point	3273 °C (5923.40 °F)
Melting point	1313 °C (2395.40 °F)

Gadolinium has a special place in the history of the lanthanides, as revealed by its name. Ask a chemist who the most important figure in the history of the lanthanoids is, and they may well answer with one name: that of the Finnish chemist Johan Gadolin. Element number 64 is named after Gadolin, an appropriate accolade for a man who has been called 'the father of the rare earths'.

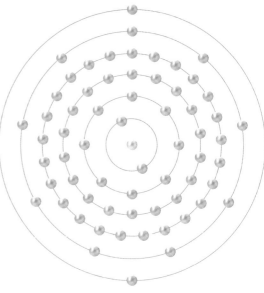

Electron configuration:
2.8.18.25.9.2

Gadolin was the chemist who chemically interrogated ytterbite – the coal-like ore that Carl Axel Arrhenius (1757–1824) had originally found – to yield yttrium. This was a breakthrough that can be reasonably said to have started the ball rolling on the discovery of the lanthanoids (despite yttrium being classified as a transition metal). Ytterbite, or as it was later known after being renamed by Klaproth, gadolinite, has an intimidating chemical formula, $((Ce,La,Nd,Y)_2FeBe_2Si_2O_{10})$, but one that shows just how important a mineral it is when it comes to sourcing the lanthanoids.

◀ *Coal-like ytterbite, which was ultimately renamed in recognition of the Finn Johan Gadolin's work with the rare-earth elements.*

There is a certain irony in Klaproth's rechristening of it too, since gadolinite has very little gadolinium in it!

In truth, of course, there are several candidates for the accolade of 'most important to the history of the lanthanoids', and one of those others is arguably the discoverer of element number 64, Jean Charles Galissard de Marignac (1817–1894), who also discovered element number 70, ytterbium.

A potentially dangerous contrast

As mentioned previously, much of the chemistry of the lanthanoids revolves around their +3 oxidation state, and it is in this state that gadolinium finds a major medical application. When MRI is used in diagnostic medicine, a substance known as a contrasting agent is often injected into the patient. The contrasting agent helps to maintain the quality of the image, and therefore aids diagnosis. What is fascinating about such agents is that they are potentially very toxic to humans. As we have seen for more than one element already (see thallium, pp. 110–11, and cadmium, pp. 80–81), many health issues can arise when one element in its ionic form mimics another, possibly replacing it or disrupting that naturally occurring ion's proper function. When one learns that Gd^{3+} has a similar size to Ca^{2+}, a ubiquitous and crucially important ion in the body

(see calcium, pp. 32–33), one can understand how many biological functions could be disrupted. For gadolinium to do the job that it is supposed to as a contrasting agent, it has to be 'tied up', or as chemists say, 'complexed', with other substances. These substances (known as ligands), 'trap' or 'lock up' the potentially problematic gadolinium ions, and prevent them from running amok in the body, while still allowing their useful attributes to be utilised. These compounds are quite extraordinary; one such ligand is capable of making eight bonds with a central metal, like an enormous spider encasing the potentially dangerous Gd cation.

⊙ *MRI uses gadolinium, but element number 64 may be on the way out in this application, as concerns over its toxicity continue to build.*

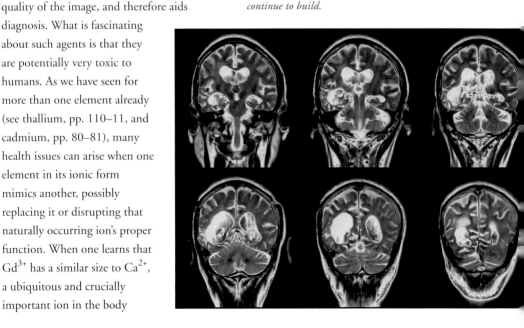

Tb Terbium

Chemical symbol	Tb
Atomic number	65
Atomic mass	158.93
Boiling point	3230 °C (5846 °F)
Melting point	1356 °C (2473 °F)

(A) *Terbium is a silvery-white, relatively soft metal that is ductile and malleable.*

The chemistry of the lanthanoids, in particular their extraction from single sources and the nightmarish difficulties of separating them all out, makes things complicated enough, but what about when elements that have almost identical names get accidently switched around? Well, it makes for even deeper confusion, and that is exactly what happened with terbium and its sister element number 68, erbium.

In keeping with the procedure of continually fine-tuning the oxides of the lanthanoids, the early 1840s saw Mosander manage to extract two more elements from an original sample of the oxide of yttrium. The year was 1843, and the oxides that Mosander pulled from the yttria were distinct from one another in terms of their colours. The first one was yellow, and he called this erbium oxide (erbia). The second one was pink, and he called it terbium oxide (terbia). Each name was derived from the Ytterby name, and because they were found at the same time and from that same source, it all seemed to make sense. Of course, with such similar names and such difficulty in distinguishing and extracting the lanthanoids, and communication being what it was almost 175 years ago, things were almost bound to go wrong – and they did.

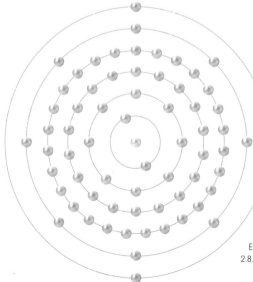

Electron configuration:
2.8.18.27.8.2

Mix and match

Sometime in the early 1860s, Delafontaine (see holmium, pp. 154–55) managed to mix up Mosander's erbia and terbia. Frankly, given the relative infancy of research into the rare earths, and the similarity of the two elements' names, it was not all that surprising. Delafontaine made the old erbia the new terbia, and vice versa. This mistake persists to this day, so when one Googles an image for erbium(III) oxide, one will find a beautiful array of pink powders and crystals, and not Mosander's original yellows.

Green and white

Old-fashioned CR (cathode-ray) tubes, used in older televisions and in fluorescent lamps, contain several phosphors that have terbium as part of their makeup. Terbium usually produces a green hue, but it can also be combined with other elements to produce white light.

More weird stuff at NOL

The Naval Ordnance Laboratory (NOL) in Maryland, USA, has already been mentioned for its role in producing one extremely odd metallic substance, nitinol (see nickel, pp. 56–57). That was in the 1950s, and twenty years later they did it again, this time with a terbium-based mixture of metals. Named in a similar way to nitinol, terfenol-D (TERbium, Fe for iron, and NOL for the name of the lab) is an alloy of terbium, iron and dysprosium that, like nitinol, has some seriously bizarre properties. This time it involves the alloy actually changing shape and size as it is exposed to a magnetic field. This property is known as magnetostriction, and it is exhibited by another alloy, galfenol (gallium and iron, of course).

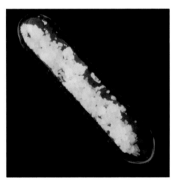

◀ *Much of the world's terbium supply is used in the production of green phosphors. A sample of terbium sulfate will glow green under ultraviolet light.*

Dy Dysprosium

Chemical symbol	Dy
Atomic number	66
Atomic mass	162.50
Boiling point	2567 °C (4653 °F)
Melting point	1412 °C (2573.60 °F)

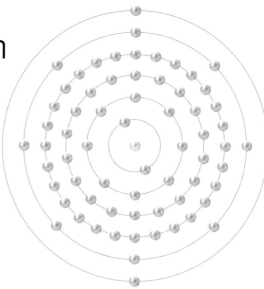

Electron configuration:
2.8.18.28.8.2

The Greek word from which the name of dysprosium is derived might as well have been applied to any one of the fifteen lanthanoids, such is their confounded elusiveness. *Dysprositos*, meaning 'hard to get at', was so named by its discoverer Paul-Émile Lecoq de Boisbaudran, at least in part for the methodology that he had to employ to get to and identify dysprosium – a painstaking process that required much patience.

⊙ *A soft, silvery metal, dysprosium is not found as the free metal in nature, rather it appears with many other lanthanoids in a variety of minerals.*

Precipitating over and over and over

Like so many of the other lanthanoids, dysprosium was discovered as a result of the continued refinement of a sample of something that was already thought to be pure, this time a sample of holmium. In this respect, the rare earths are somewhat like one of those Russian *matryoshka* dolls, where one just keeps popping out from inside another. In order to make that happen, one needed to be a pretty persistent chemist, especially given the range (or rather the lack) of chemical analysis and separation techniques that were available in the late 1800s. Enter a Frenchman whose name has appeared several times before in this book. The story goes that Lecoq de Boisbaudran had repeatedly to put the sample in solution, and then perform more than fifty tedious precipitations using various acids, before he got to a sample of a compound of element number 66. A sample of the pure element was not produced until the early 1950s, via the ion-exchange method developed by Frank Spedding (1902–84) at the University of Iowa, USA. At this point, Spedding deserves a special mention.

Spedding speeds the research

Because it had been so difficult to obtain pure and significant-sized samples of the lanthanoid elements, there was unlikely to be any research into their chemistry, and therefore their potential uses, until a somewhat economical and practical method for processing and separating the ores was developed. As an example of Frank Spedding's important work, one 1950 paper he co-authored was entitled, 'Separation of Rare Earths by Ion Exchange. IV. Further Investigations Concerning Variables Involved in the Separation of Samarium, Neodymium and Praseodymium'. Spedding and his team's efforts were so vital in extracting the lanthanoids, and therefore in finding uses for them, that his impact cannot be underestimated. In fact, Karl A. Gschneidner Jr. (1930–2016) – himself a world renowned expert who was known as 'Mr. Rare Earth' for his extensive knowledge of the elements, and who had worked under Spedding – described his mentor as the rightful 'father of the rare earths'.

▲ *Frank Spedding (right) with the physicist Niels Bohr. Spedding was a pioneer in the separation of the lanthanoids.*

Got it. Now what?

So much for actually getting to dysprosium; but what about its uses? Whether it is as doping material in specialised ceramics, or as small parts of various magnetic materials, or as a neutron absorber, like the other lanthanoids, all of element 66's applications are quite specialised. One of the more mainstream uses of dysprosium has been in the form of the triiodide and tribromide compounds, DyI_3 and $DyBr_3$, respectively, in metal-halide lighting.

◀ *Dysprosium is used in metal halide lighting. The intensity and colour of the light can be controlled by varying the composition of the compounds and gases present.*

Ho Holmium

Chemical symbol	Ho
Atomic number	67
Atomic mass	164.93
Boiling point	2700 °C (4892 °F)
Melting point	1474 °C (2685.20 °F)

Although it is not one of the four elements that was named after that famous town of Ytterby in Sweden (see yttrium, pp. 62–63), holmium nevertheless has its roots firmly ensconced in Scandinavia. As the infernally complicated ores of the lanthanoids were purified, holmium was a result of finer and finer separation. Just when chemists thought that they had got to the bottom of things, out popped another rare earth element!

Most sources give joint credit for the discovery of holmium to Marc Delafontaine (1837–1911), Jacques-Louis Soret (1827–1890) and Per Teodor Cleve (1840–1905) in 1878. The confusion arises because of the time period that we are dealing with here (communication was hardly instantaneous), and the fact that when it comes to the birth of so many of the lanthanoids, absolute certainty is a tricky thing. Holmium came from erbium samples, which in turn contained yttrium. Later still, holmium samples yielded dysprosium. Either way, one could say that the Swiss pair of Delafontaine and Soret lost out, and that Cleve really won the day, because, like hafnium (see pp. 82–83), the name for element 67 is derived from the Latin name for a Scandinavian city, this time Holmia, or Stockholm. Cleve's work was carried out in Uppsala in Sweden, and had the Swiss come out on top, then there would probably be a completely different name for element 67. Delafontaine had favoured the name 'phillipium' for the new element, in honour of a benefactor of his, but once again the relative difficulty of long-distance communication in the late 1800s led to some further confusion. At the time, Soret was in Geneva in Switzerland and Delafontaine was in Chicago. Soret did not know

Holmium is named after the Latin name for Stockholm, Holmia. Sweden has many connections to the lanthanoids, not least of all the town of Ytterby.

that Delafontaine had already proposed a name for the new element, so he in turn suggested one: 'element X'. In the end, none of this mattered, and holmium seems a little less cold than simply 'X'!

More magnets, more lasers

As is consistent with the theme of similarities among the lanthanides, holmium has a couple of close connections to one of its near neighbours, neodymium. First, holmium has some curious magnetic properties. It is the lanthanide that exhibits the strongest paramagnetism, meaning that when it is placed in an external magnetic field, it has the ability to concentrate the magnetic field to the greatest degree. This superpower is put to use in MRI machines in hospitals, which allow detailed pictures of the inside of the body to be taken.

Second, also like element number 60, holmium is used as a doping agent for the production of solid-state lasers. Ho:YAG crystals, as they are known, are once more based upon the yttrium aluminium garnet crystals (see p. 63), with tiny amounts of holmium introduced. These lasers are used in surgical applications where precise cutting is needed, and can destroy tumours with incredible accuracy, leading to very little collateral damage to healthy tissue. They have also been used in urologic medicine in destroying urinary stones and in the treatment of prostate disorders.

(▶) *Although holmium is one of the least utilised elements, it finds important applications in medicine, in both laser and imaging technology.*

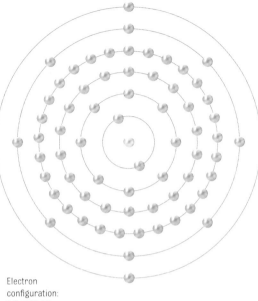

Electron configuration: 2.8.18.29.8.2

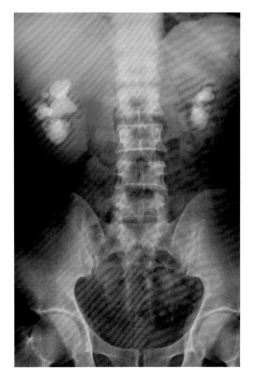

Er Erbium

Chemical symbol	Er
Atomic number	68
Atomic mass	167.26
Boiling point	2868 °C (5194 °F)
Melting point	1529 °C (2784 °F)

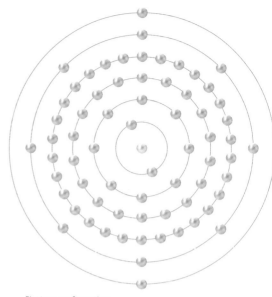

Electron configuration:
2.8.18.30.8.2

Having been extracted and confused with terbium right from the beginning (see terbium, pp. 150–51), erbium (or more accurately erbia) itself became the source of yet another of the lanthanoids. After Mosander had finished with his erbium oxide, it was left for Marignac to pull ytterbium (see pp. 160–61) from it. After all the confusion, it's nice to finally get some clarity and shed some light on erbium in its own right.

Pink and green

Erbium's pale pink salts are really quite stunning, and among chemists their colour is probably their best known and most loved attribute. White light is a mixture of all of the colours of the rainbow, the classic ROYGBIV (red, orange, yellow, green, blue, indigo and violet), and it's that fact that accounts for the colour of all objects. For any compound to exhibit colour, it must absorb certain wavelengths of light and reflect others.

◀ Erbium oxide, Er_2O_3, has a very distinctive pink colour. It has a number of optical and electrical applications.

Erbium happens to absorb light in the green part of the spectrum, with a wavelength of around 530 nanometres. As the green light is absorbed by the erbium ions, what's left is reflected. Since pink is a complementary colour to green, pink light is reflected. Erbium's pink colour can be utilised in the aesthetic tinting of glass, and in glazes used for ceramics, but it also has a practical application.

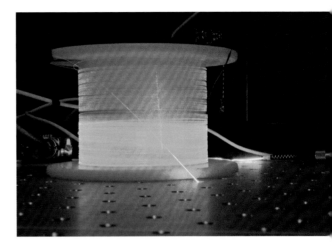

Ⓐ *Erbium-doped optical fibres are used for long-range communications. The erbium serves to amplify the optical signals.*

Eyewear and safety

As well as absorbing light in the green part of the spectrum, erbium also has the ability to absorb infrared light. This is particularly useful if one wants to extract infrared light from an incoming source in order to protect one's eyes, and as a result, erbium-impregnated safety eyewear has been developed.

More doping means better communications

Erbium's relationship with electromagnetic radiation doesn't end with green and infrared light. Like several of its lanthanoid cousins, a relatively tiny amount of erbium, when introduced as an impurity, can dramatically enhance the properties of the host material. The process, known as doping, is put to use in many areas, such as in semiconductors and lasers. Element number 68 is used in what are known as EDFAs, or erbium-doped fibre amplifiers. Here, erbium helps the optical fibres to increase the intensity of signals carried in the cables. Under normal circumstances, the light that travels in any optical fibre will undergo

scattering as the photons crash into the physical structures inside the glass. When this happens, the signal is weakened significantly, and the distance that the light can travel is limited. In a complex process of energy absorption and release, Er^{3+} ions are able to magnify the incoming signal, meaning that the cables become increasingly efficient and can be longer.

Super single-molecule magnets

Erbium is at the literal centre of a relatively new technology known as single-molecule magnets, or SMMs. Erbium atoms sandwiched between organic molecules in organometallic structures have the potential to replace conventional magnets, since their storage capacity can exceed that of normal magnetic storage used in computing by several thousandfold.

Tm Thulium

Chemical symbol	Tm
Atomic number	69
Atomic mass	168.93
Boiling point	1950 °C (3542 °F)
Melting point	1545 °C (2813 °F)

Another element that came from an impure erbium oxide, thulium was discovered by Per Teodor Cleve in 1879. Cleve was a Swede, and seemingly not content with paying homage to his native country by naming element number 67 after its capital city, he named number 69 thulium, after Thule, an ancient name for the northernmost region of Europe, which many people now agree was probably part of Scandinavia (although it's debatable).

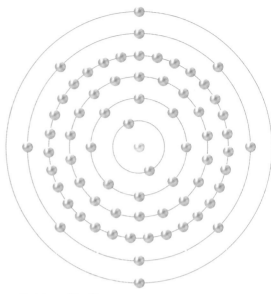

Electron configuration:
2.8.18.31.8.2

Replacing Gd?

In the portrait of gadolinium (see pp. 148–49) we looked at its use in MRI contrasting agents, along with concerns about its potential toxic effects on humans. In recent years there has been increased concern over the potential for gadolinium ions to escape their ligand cages and enter the body. As a result, scientists have been seeking alternatives to gadolinium, and thulium is one such potential replacement. It has been tested, with some success, in this role, along with element number 66, dysprosium.

◁ *Malleable and ductile, thulium metal is soft and silver-coloured, but will discolour rapidly on exposure to air.*

X-ray source

Thulium was proposed as a source of X-rays as early as the mid-1950s. Tm-170 is the isotope in question, and it is not one that is naturally occurring. It was originally produced in a heavy-water nuclear reactor. Thulium is an ideal material for low-intensity, low-tech, simple and portable X-ray machines, such as those found in dentists' offices, and those used for detecting cracks in industrial equipment. With a half-life of just under 129 days, a small piece of thulium can remain useful as an X-ray source for a couple of years before it needs to be replaced.

⊛ *Thulium has found use in low-intensity, portable X-ray machines, such as those found in dentists' offices.*

Same as the others

In multiple connections to several of its other lanthanoid companions, thulium has some fairly narrow and specialised uses. Like europium, it is found as an anti-counterfeiting agent in euro banknotes; like neodymium and holmium, it can be used as a doping agent in YAG crystals for medical cutting lasers; like dysprosium, it has been used in metal halide lamps, producing emission lines in the green part of the spectrum; and like lutetium, thulium is rather rare and expensive, but with so few large-scale uses, the demand for the element is quite low.

Famously (at least among people who care about such things), one of the most important science writers on the elements, John Emsley (b. 1938), has been quoted by

Theodore Gray (b. 1964) in his book, *The Elements: A Visual Exploration of Every Known Atom in the Universe*, as saying that thulium is 'the least significant element there is'. One can debate that subjective statement if one likes, but given its relative obscurity (it's only the sixty-first most abundant element) and its relatively few applications, it is hard to argue convincingly against it. Take a look at most textbooks that deal with the elements and their chemistry and you'll often find a simple reference that says something like, 'see lanthanoids'. When one turns to those pages, if any words are devoted to thulium specifically, then they are likely to point to the history of element number 69 and not much else.

Yb Ytterbium

Chemical symbol	Yb
Atomic number	70
Atomic mass	173.05
Boiling point	1196 °C (2185 °F)
Melting point	819 °C (1506.20 °F)

If you think that an element with such an odd-looking name simply must be related to the other element on the periodic table with an equally odd-looking one, then you'd be right. As the final of the four elements to be named after the Swedish town of Ytterby, element number 70 forever has that connection to element number 39, yttrium (as well as to terbium and erbium).

In fact, and appropriately enough, impure samples of yttrium gave up erbium, number 68, before samples of it gave up ytterbium. When, in 1878, the Swiss chemist Jean Charles Galissard de Marignac isolated the new oxide, he named the element in such a way that it paid homage to both yttrium and erbium – again, entirely appropriately. Of course, you won't be astonished to learn that like so many of the other lanthanoids there was a mild dispute, an alternative name, and a discussion about priority, involving Carl Auer von Welsbach, who wished to call it 'aldebaranium'.

+2 to +3

As we have seen in many examples of the chemistry of the elements in this section, the majority of lanthanoid chemistry is dominated by the +3 oxidation state. Ytterbium is one of the lanthanoids that is a little different, inasmuch as there is some significant +2 oxidation state chemistry associated with it. If one is totally honest, though, that is a little misleading. The main characteristic of those compounds in the +2 oxidation state is that they are strong reducing agents, a class of chemicals used in an important classification of chemical reactions called redox reactions. When a substance acts as a reducing agent, it gives away electrons. Since electrons are negatively charged, the substance that is giving the electrons away, the reducing agent, becomes increasingly positive in the

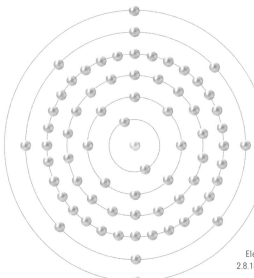

Electron configuration:
2.8.18.32.8.2

process. When Yb^{2+} ions act in this manner, they are doing no more than exhibiting a strong tendency to become Yb^{3+}. An example of such a reaction is the willingness of Yb^{2+} to react with water to produce flammable hydrogen gas.

All change

Bright, shiny, ductile and malleable, ytterbium is a fairly standard-looking metal. It has a variety of naturally occurring isotopes with masses ranging from 168 to 176, with ytterbium-174 being the most abundant. Those isotopes, taken together with their relative natural abundances considered,

used to give an average atomic mass for ytterbium of 173.054. That was until, in 2015, that mass was revised by the IUPAC to 173.045, when a reassessment of the isotopic abundance of the element was incorporated into the new calculation. Proof that the periodic table is a living, ever-changing thing.

Clocking in

Ytterbium has recently created a lot of interest in the world of ultra-accurate timekeeping. Even though caesium atomic clocks (see pp. 22–23) are considered accurate to one second in approximately every 300 million years, apparently we can do better! Scientists are continuing to refine what are known as optical clocks, this time using a single ytterbium ion, cooled to close to absolute zero with a laser.

⊙ *Ytterbium finds a specialist application in atomic clocks, where it is set to improve upon even the ultra-accurate caesium versions.*

Lu Lutetium

Chemical symbol	Lu
Atomic number	71
Atomic mass	174.97
Boiling point	6156 °F (3402 °C)
Melting point	3025.40 °F (1663 °C)

There are several elements that have a French connection. A couple of them are fairly obvious, with gallium and francium named after the Latin and the modern name for France, respectively. Then there's the whole Marie Curie link. Element number 71 is one of these elements too, but you'd have to be a scholar of language to know that the Latin name for Paris was *Lutetia*.

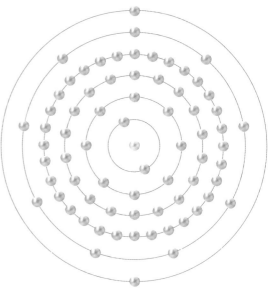

Electron configuration:
2.8.18.32.9.2

So, why Paris? Well, like so many of the elements in the lanthanoid collection, number 71 had a tortuous start to its life. Lutetium didn't arrive until 1907, making it the last of the lanthanoids to be discovered, and the ultimate credit goes to Georges Urbain (1872–1938) who was, you've guessed it, a native of Paris. The discovery was not concluded until after Charles James (1880–1928) in the United States had isolated a large amount of the element – but never published his findings – and Carl Auer von Welsbach (see praseodymium, pp. 138–39) had done something similar in Germany. Auer von Welsbach was a little more confident, and perhaps a little more audacious than the

◀ *The French connection: Lutetium was named after the Latin name for Paris, the native city of its discoverer, George Urbain.*

English-born James, and went as far as to name his element. He called it cassiopeium – another celestial reference, this time to a constellation – and this name persisted in the literature, especially in Germany, through the 1950s.

◁ Lutetium is a silvery-white metal. Its separation and purification is among the most difficult of all of the lanthanoids.

Where is Lu?

Lutetium's positioning on the periodic table remains open to question. If you look at the current IUPAC periodic table, you will see it where you are probably expecting it, at the far right of the 4f block that has been separated out before the main body of the table. Since it is the last element in the lanthanoid collection, that's right, right? Well, not so fast. Lutetium is sometimes placed in group 3 of the periodic table, underneath yttrium, element number 39, and to the left of hafnium, element

number 72. Many papers have been written on this matter, and many angry arguments have been conducted on the pages of chemistry journals, but that's not something that I'm going to get into here, other than to note the following: Lutetium is a hard, silvery-white metal and its ions are the smallest of the Ln^{3+} ions, a result of what is known as the lanthanide contraction. The size of the Lu^{3+} ion makes it quite like that of Sc^{3+} and Y^{3+}.

Rare and expensive

Lutetium is the rarest of the lanthanoids and that makes it expensive – very expensive. However, this is somewhat offset by the fact that lutetium has very few uses and therefore is not in especially high demand. Its use as a catalyst component in petroleum cracking and other industrial processes lends some credence to its potential positioning among the transition metals, but then again, much like lutetium's fellow lanthanoids, it can be used as a dopant in garnet crystals, this time in gadolinium gallium garnet (GGG), which is used in computer memory hardware. In short, lutetium doesn't really know its rightful place.

⊙ There remains a debate over the correct position of Lutetium in the periodic table. Should it sit at the end of the lanthanoid series, or should it be a group-3 element?

Actinoids

As we shall see, with one or two notable exceptions, the application of the actinoids is almost solely confined to their radioactive nature. Either as instruments of war, or as nuclear fuels, the instability of their nuclei is at the literal centre of both their menace and their delight. Harnessing that power has created not only chemical conflict, but immense political conflict. The actinoids are indeed a collection of elements with a significant influence on human history.

On the following pages:

Ac	Actinium	U	Uranium
Th	Thorium	Pu	Plutonium
Pa	Protactinum	Cm	Curium

What *exactly* are we dealing with?

The actinoids are a series of fifteen radioactive elements that start with element number 89, actinium, and pass through to element number 103, lawrencium. It is good to establish that fact first, since as with the lanthanoids/lanthanides (pp. 132–63), throughout history there has been some confusion over the collective name for this band of elements, and even disputes over which elements to include. The first problem arises when one considers the literal meaning of the word *actinoid*. In the strictest sense, actinoid means 'like actinium' and therefore should really exclude actinium from the list. So why did we start using a piece of terminology that was problematic in this manner? Well, at least in part because of a *different* problem with the original name for the group, the actinides. When used in chemistry, the -*ide* ending refers to a negative ion such as fluoride F⁻ or chloride Cl⁻. As such, it was deemed inappropriate for use as a

Ⓐ *The familiar sight of massive cooling towers at a nuclear power plant. The actinoids are renowned for their radioactive nature and associated applications.*

collective term for an alliance of neutral elements. In reality, since both actinoid and actinide have their own issues, and since each has a history of use, both remain acceptable in most contexts, although the official IUPAC Red Book prefers 'actinoids'.

A closer look at the elements in the set reveals two distinct subsets. First, there are those that occur in nature in relatively significant amounts – this is relative, since none of the actinoids are especially abundant. This list includes thorium, uranium and protactinium. Then there are the remainder of the actinoids, which are far less abundant and present on earth in only tiny amounts, often only as products of natural radioactive decay or artificially produced in laboratories.

Ac Actinium

Chemical symbol	Ac
Atomic number	89
Atomic mass	227 (longest-living isotope)
Boiling point	3198 °C (5788 °F)
Melting point	1051 °C (1923.80 °F)

The current importance of actinium in the world is extremely limited. It is used in a few medical applications, and perhaps research will ultimately lead to some incredibly important future use, but for now, not so much. Having said that, as the first, and therefore as a somewhat representative element in the actinoid series, actinium allows one to make some interesting observations about radioactivity.

Discovered by André Debierne (1874–1949) in Paris in 1899, any potential that actinium might have had as an element of significant use to mankind was scuppered by two key characteristics. First, it is one of the least abundant elements in the earth's crust. That fact alone means that even if it did not possess the second characteristic, ferocious radioactivity, it would be tricky to put the element to much practical use. When one does consider actinium's radioactivity, therein lies the second major problem.

Alpha-cell attack

Actinium has been used in a cancer treatment procedure known as Medical Actinium for Therapeutic Treatment, or MATT. Actinium-225 is an alpha-emitter, as it decays to bismuth-213, emitting alpha particles along the way. The radionuclide can be attached to a targeting agent, which can seek specific cancerous cells, and the alpha particles can then destroy the cancer.

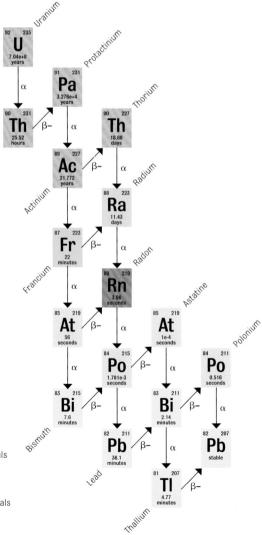

- ● Actinoids
- ● Alkaline earth metals
- ● Alkali metals
- ● Noble gases
- ● Metalloids
- ● Post-transition metals

The advantages of MATT are that the half-lives of the actinium isotope and its daughter nuclides are short (meaning residual radiation after treatment is not a big concern), and the alpha radiation is not especially penetrating (meaning collateral cell damage is minimal). The disadvantage is, of course, the chronic lack of availability of actinium.

An unstable element

All of the actinoid elements are radioactive, but in the case of actinium, there are no stable isotopes. This means that every atomic version of the element, no matter how many neutrons are tied up in the nucleus with the consistent eighty-nine protons, is unstable, and will quickly disintegrate into other elements. All of the isotopes of actinium reported have short half-lives (ranging from nanoseconds to a few years), and this contributes to the virtual complete absence of the element in the earth's crust. Starting with uranium-235, actinium is produced as the heavier and more abundant actinide decays; however, within a very short period of time those actinium atoms decay further, and it's gone. It is really only actinium-227, with a half-life of approximately 22 years, that we have any significant knowledge of.

Electron configuration: 2.8.18.32.18.9.2

◉ *The actinium decay chain shows how nuclei are converted from one element to another by the emission of either alpha or beta particles. Alpha emission reduces the number of protons and hence the atomic number, while beta emission increases each.*

As a result of the relatively long half-life of actinium-227, it is the isotope that is most likely to be encountered naturally. Of course, 'relative' is a term that suggests that such a half-life is actually not very long at all, and that naturally occurring actinium is super-rare, decaying as it does to other nuclei. What little actinium there is on earth is found in conjunction with the far more abundant actinoid uranium. As a result, any actinium needed for research purposes needs to be prepared artificially by the bombardment of radium-226 with neutrons to give radium-227:

$$^{226}_{88}\text{Ra} + {}^{1}_{0}\text{n} \rightarrow {}^{227}_{88}\text{Ra}$$

Then the radium-227 decays via beta emission to produce actinium-227:

$$^{227}_{88}\text{Ra} \rightarrow {}^{227}_{89}\text{Ac} + {}^{0}_{-1}\beta$$

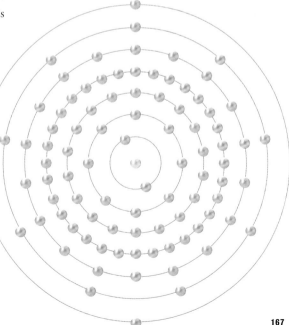

Th Thorium

Chemical symbol	Th
Atomic number	90
Atomic mass	232.04
Boiling point	4788 °C (8650 °F)
Melting point	1750 °C (3182 °F)

Another dangerously radioactive element (and an element that yields a host of dangerously radioactive isotopes through its decay series), thorium has a bizarre history of 'medicinal' applications very similar to that of radium. As a modern element, thorium finds use In nuclear reactors, but as the 1930s-marketed health elixir Radithor, it promised (along with radium), some tremendous health benefits.

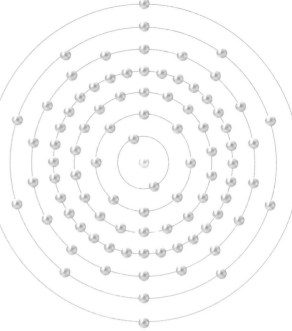

Electron configuration:
2.8.18.32.18.10.2

Jöns Jakob Berzelius first recognised thorium as an element in 1829, when he identified it as a new substance in a mineral containing thorium silicate. Named after the Norse god of thunder, Thor, thorium had to wait for almost another three-quarters of a century before it came into its own.

▶ *Swedish chemist J. J. Berzelius had a hand in many elemental discoveries and is considered one of the founders of modern chemistry.*

Radithor

As we saw with radium (pp. 38–39), in the first few years of the twentieth century the recently discovered phenomenon of radioactivity was being touted as a new wonder medicine. Radithor was just one such item in an extensive list of long-since debunked radioactive quackery. Of course, the claims surrounding Radithor's benefits as a 'triple distilled' radiation-infused water proved not to be remotely true. In this respect, Radithor was no different from the Radium Ore Revigator. However, the high-profile death of the prominent American socialite

Eben Byers (1880–1932), a well-known and voracious consumer of Radithor, helped to provoke a much closer look at the catastrophic effects that such products could have on the human body. Accounts of the structural demise of Byers's jaw and skull make for some gruesome reading, and the dire warnings surrounding his predicament led to significant changes in the regulation of such radioactive 'health' products.

◀ *Radithor is an example of a product that falls into the category of radioactive quackery – radioactive materials incorrectly promoted as remedies for various ailments.*

The Radioactive Boy Scout

Moving forward from the dubious use of thorium in misguided 'medicinal' remedies, the element did find a legitimate use in gas lighting. As one of the elements infused, in its oxide form, into the mantles of gas lamps, the thorium compound would emit a bright, white light. Thorium-infused gas mantles were a favourite purchase of the infamous 'Radioactive Boy Scout', David Hahn (1976–2016), whose exploits defy belief. Hahn managed to accumulate a frighteningly large collection

of various radioactive materials in an attempt to build several nuclear devices. (His story is documented in Ken Silverstein's 2004 book, *The Radioactive Boy Scout: The Frightening True Story of a Whiz Kid and His Homemade Nuclear Reactor.*)

Future fuel?

Thorium was also alloyed with magnesium to increase the material's strength and resistance to high temperature, but increasing regulation in relation to the shipping and use of the radioactive metal has long since curtailed most of that particular activity. In thermal breeder nuclear reactors, thorium-232 is used to create uranium-233 that can then be used as a nuclear fuel, but the technology remains beset with technical difficulties that currently prevent it from being a widespread, commercially viable enterprise. Thorium's potential as a nuclear fuel remains tempting, though, since it is so much more abundant on earth than uranium, and as such, may prove to be an important, viable material of the future.

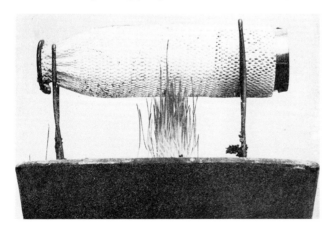

◀ *This experiment, featured in* Popular Science *in 1909, explored the effect of radiation from an unburned thorium gas mantle on the germination and growth of grass seed.*

Pa Protactinium

Electron configuration: 2.8.18.32.20.9.2

Chemical symbol	Pa
Atomic number	91
Atomic mass	231.04
Boiling point	4027 °C (7280 °F)
Melting point	1572 °C (2861.60 °F)

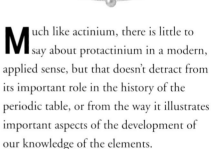

Eka-tantalum, or if one prefers, maybe brevium, UX₂, or perhaps even protoactinium, it doesn't really matter – you are talking about element number 91 whichever name you choose. A complex history of attempted discovery and clumsy naming precedes the modern moniker for element number 91, all fraught with confusion and stumbling indecision – in that respect, one might say that as the history of protactinium goes, so goes the history of the whole periodic table!

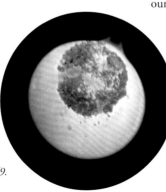

▶ *The darker area at the centre of the photo is a sample of protactinium-233, photographed in the light from its own radioactive emission (the lighter area), at the National Reactor Testing Station in Idaho, USA, circa 1969.*

M uch like actinium, there is little to say about protactinium in a modern, applied sense, but that doesn't detract from its important role in the history of the periodic table, or from the way it illustrates important aspects of the development of our knowledge of the elements.

Isotope confusion

As seen elsewhere (scandium, gallium and germanium), Dmitri Mendeleev had predicted the existence of several as yet undiscovered elements; one of those was an element that he said would sit between thorium and uranium. With hindsight, and the knowledge of Moseley's atomic number system, that element would have to be element number 91, ultimately called protactinium. Honestly, though, we are getting ahead of ourselves here.

Much of the confusion surrounding the discovery of elements in this part of the periodic table, and at this time in history, can be put down to the fact that the neutron had yet to be discovered, and therefore the idea of isotopes had not yet been formulated. As such, substances that appeared like they just might be something entirely new turned out with hindsight to be different isotopes of already known elements.

UX_2, aka brevium, was observed by Kazimierz Fajans (1887–1975) and Oswald Helmuth Göhring (1889–c. 1915) in 1913. The name UX_2 was the second in a series of names given to particles that originated from the radioactive decay of uranium. The first of those was named UX (and later UX1) and proved to be what we now know as thorium-234. The name 'brevium' was chosen for UX_2 to reflect the short time that the element existed, and although accurate, proved to be unfortunate for the two Germans since 'discovering' such a short-lived species made confirmation and further study next to impossible. A few years later, element number 91, or perhaps more accurately, an isotope of element number 91 with a longer half-life, came to the attention of Lise Meitner (1878–1968) and Otto Hahn (1879–1968). In 1918 they published a paper reporting their results that suggested the name 'protoactinium' for the 'new' element, a name derived from the Greek *protos*, meaning 'first'. This was supposed to

▲ *Lise Meitner and Otto Hahn in the laboratory. Element number 109, meitnerium, is named after Meitner in recognition of her work on nuclear fission.*

denote the fact that it was an isotope that ultimately produced the already known actinium. That was all well and good, but the name didn't exactly roll off the tongue, so the IUPAC settled on the slightly easier to pronounce 'protactinium' in 1949.

Long and short lives

Returning to brevium and protoactinium, we see the significance of each of these discoveries in the current knowledge that protactinium exists as only two isotopes of any significance. Protactinium-234 (the original brevium) has a half-life of just under seven hours and is a beta emitter, whereas the other isotope is protactinium-231, which has a half-life of close to 33,000 years and is an alpha emitter. Hardly surprising that the credit for discovery and naming is less than clear, depending on the source.

U Uranium

Chemical symbol	U
Atomic number	92
Atomic mass	283.03
Boiling point	4131 °C (7468 °F)
Melting point	1132 °C (2070 °F)

After a pretty slow start to its life as an element, uranium became a vitally important one, since it helped to birth the Nuclear Age. Uranium's influence truly began in 1896, with the discovery of radioactivity. Following this, uranium went from being an element with little significance in the grand scheme, to arguably one of the most important of the twentieth century and beyond.

After Martin Heinrich Klaproth discovered uranium in 1789, not much happened with the element until, in 1896, the French chemist Henri Becquerel (1852–1908) discovered radioactivity as a result of the spontaneous decay of some uranium salts. Becquerel was investigating phosphorescence and X-rays when he noticed that photographic plates that had been exposed to the uranium salts but no sunlight still developed images. He concluded that the uranium salts were emitting some form of radiation. After the dawn of radioactivity, the rest is, as they say, history. In the 1930s and '40s, work by various scientists, both inside and outside the US government's Manhattan Project (the research project designed to develop nuclear weapons), helped to cement uranium's place as an element of vital importance, when the potential for nuclear fission was proposed. In fission reactions, heavy nuclei such as uranium's are split open, and the enormous amount of energy that accompanies such reactions was to be the key to uranium's rise in importance as a potential fuel.

Little Boy

For use in the *Little Boy* nuclear bomb that was dropped on Hiroshima, Japan, on the morning of August 6, 1945, American scientists needed one particular isotope of uranium, U-235. U-235 is the isotope that when bombarded with neutrons, splits apart to form lighter nuclei and more neutrons. This process, known as fission,

◄ Henri Becquerel's contribution to our understanding of radioactivity is immortalised in the name of the SI unit for radioactivity: the becquerel (Bq).

produces energy, and since neutrons are produced in the process, it can initiate a chain reaction that releases almost unfathomable amounts of energy. The uncontrolled release of that energy is the essence of a nuclear bomb. Uranium is relatively plentiful on earth, being the forty-sixth most abundant element, and exists as three naturally occurring isotopes: U-238, U-235 and U-234. However, the U-238 isotope makes up over 99 percent of the supply, and therefore, before a critical mass (the mass required to sustain the chain reaction) of the 235 isotope can be obtained, it must go through a process of enrichment to increase the percentage of U-235 present in any given sample.

Ⓐ A model of Little Boy, the atomic bomb that was dropped on Hiroshima from the B-29 Superfortress aircraft Enola Gay.

Electron configuration:
2.8.18.32.21.9.2

Fiestaware

Long before its use in nuclear weapons and as a nuclear fuel, compounds of uranium were originally added to pottery and glass in order to produce colourful glazes. In fact, a popular and highly collectable dinnerware range called Fiesta was manufactured in the United States using a number of such glazes. The orange-red colours of Fiesta dinnerware used to contain significant amounts of uranium oxides, and this led to the cups, saucers and plates having detectable radioactivity counts!

Ⓥ Some glazes used for the twentieth-century dinnerware known as Fiestaware were manufactured using uranium oxide and have been found to be radioactive.

Pu Plutonium

Chemical symbol	Pu
Atomic number	94
Atomic mass	244 (longest-living isotope)
Boiling point	3228 °C (5842 °F)
Melting point	639.4 °C (1182.9 °F)

Ⓐ *The mushroom cloud observed over the Japanese city of Nagasaki following the dropping of the* Fat Man *atomic bomb in 1945.*

Like uranium, plutonium is without doubt an element that impacted world history. As a fissile material, Pu-239 can provide a sustainable nuclear chain reaction, releasing enormous amounts of energy in the process. The *Fat Man* plutonium bomb that was dropped on the Japanese city of Nagasaki on the morning of August 9, 1945, three days after the uranium-based *Little Boy*, effectively ended the Second World War.

Planetary body

The element was first synthesised in Berkeley, California, in late 1940. However, due to national security concerns, the Americans wanted to prevent word of its discovery getting out, and by the time it was formally announced in 1946, Nagasaki had already been flattened. Plutonium is the third element in a series that were named after planets (uranium after Uranus and neptunium after Neptune both

precede Pu). There is virtually no plutonium present in the earth's crust, so it has to be manufactured in nuclear facilities. In the early 1940s, the US government needed a significant amount of plutonium in order to build a nuclear bomb, and they set up a production facility to make element number 94. The nuclear reactions that they used are shown below.

$$^{238}_{92}U + ^{1}_{0}n \rightarrow ^{239}_{92}U$$

$$^{239}_{92}U \rightarrow ^{239}_{93}Np + ^{0}_{-1}\beta$$

$$^{239}_{93}Np \rightarrow ^{239}_{94}Pu + ^{0}_{-1}\beta$$

Ⓑ *A model of* Fat Man, *the atomic bomb that was dropped on Nagasaki from the B-29 Superfortress aircraft,* Bockscar.

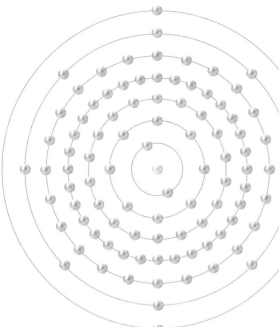

Electron configuration:
2.8.18.32.24.8.2

is struck with a neutron, the products of the nuclear event include energy and more neutrons. These additional neutrons can go on to strike other Pu atoms, and a chain reaction occurs. The cumulative energy from each minuscule atomic event is massive, and causes a colossal explosion. In the case of Nagasaki, it produced sufficient energy to kill tens of thousands of people and to obliterate a large city with the detonation of a single bomb.

Peacetime plutonium

In times of relative peace, the nuclear power of plutonium is harnessed for the production of nuclear energy. One type of nuclear reactor uses a fuel that is a compound of plutonium, plutonium dioxide (PuO_2). Combined with the equivalent oxide of uranium, UO_2, the fuel is commonly known as MOX, or mixed oxide fuel.

In the first reaction, U-238 captures a neutron to become the heavier isotope, U-239. In the second reaction, that isotope emits a beta particle to become an isotope of neptunium, element 93. In the final nuclear event, another beta particle is released, and neptunium is converted to Pu-239. It's this isotope of plutonium that was used in the *Fat Man* nuclear bomb.

Such a bomb works via a nuclear chain reaction that is initiated with neutrons. When an atom of Pu-239

(▶) *Nuclear fuel pellets like this one are often made of MOX, mixed oxides of plutonium and uranium. The U and Pu in the pellets are the source of the nuclear reaction that takes place in the reactor.*

Cm Curium

Chemical symbol	Cm
Atomic number	96
Atomic mass	247 (longest-living isotope)
Boiling point	*c.* 3100 °C (5612 °F)
Melting point	1345 °C (2453 °F)

Curium is noteworthy if for no other reason that it is named (in part) after the woman who discovered two other elements, Marie Curie. I say 'in part', since formally element number 96 is dedicated to both her and her husband, Pierre, but Marie's impact as a female in the otherwise almost exclusively male-dominated world of the history of radioactivity, the discovery of the elements and the periodic table in general, is worthy of particular recognition.

KEY FIGURE

MARIE CURIE

1867–1934

Native Pole Marie Curie and her French husband Pierre were pioneering scientists in the field of radioactivity. They were awarded the 1903 Nobel Prize in Physics for their work. In 1911 Marie Curie was awarded the Nobel Prize in Chemistry for her discoveries of radium and polonium. In the process, she became the first person to receive two Nobel Prizes. The ultimate honour in terms of elements was bestowed upon the Curies when element number 96 was named curium in recognition of their work.

The Curies' work in discovering two other elements (polonium and radium) is one thing, but the ultimate prize for any element-seeker is to have an element named after him- or herself. In the early days of elemental discovery there was a tremendous amount of skullduggery and downright lying and cheating. This unethical behaviour took a number of different forms. In some cases it was just a simple dispute over who had found the element first (known as priority); in other cases it was a matter of a more subtle subterfuge; and in further disputes there was the chance of an

international incident, as elements took on two completely different names depending on whether one lived in the Soviet Union or in the United States, or in England or in France. All of this backstabbing largely came to an end when, in 1947, the IUPAC stepped in and said 'Enough is enough'. The rules that they initially established for naming have evolved over time, to the point where now, new elements must be named after one of the following:

- a mythological concept or character (including an astronomical object)
- a mineral or similar substance
- a place or geographical region
- a property of the element
- a scientist

A premature announcement

When, in 1944, curium was synthesised for the first time, no such specific rules existed, but that was the least of the problems associated with curium's announcement to the world. Curium was found as a result of research into nuclear weapons in the context of the Manhattan Project and the Second World War. As such, discoveries were bound by concerns over American national security, and announcements of new elements via the usual channels of scientific journals had to wait. In fact, in the end, the co-discoverer of curium, Glenn Seaborg, made a casual announcement on a children's radio programme when a kid asked him if any new elements had recently been discovered. He answered in a somewhat matter-of-fact manner by saying, 'Why, yes, yes they have!' This was just a few days before the official announcement was originally planned to be made.

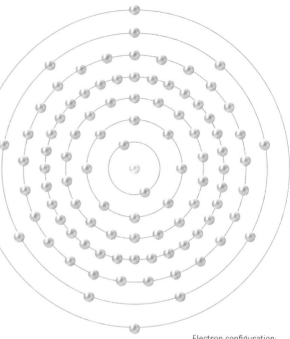

Electron configuration:
2.8.18.32.25.9.2

An element of few uses

Outside of its historical significance, curium's practical applications are extremely limited. As an alpha particle emitter it has a few uses (curium-242 can be used as a source of thermal energy since its decay is associated with an unusually high production of heat), but the unpleasant radioactive nature of most of its decay products means that it is not suitable for any extensive applications.

◀ *Glenn Seaborg had an extraordinary career in nuclear chemistry, and in particular in the synthesis of new elements. He was honoured by having element number 106, seaborgium, named after him.*

Non-metals

Much like the term 'metalloid', the definition of a non-metal is somewhat ambiguous. The elements typically distinguished as non-metals exhibit a very wide range of properties. They include solids, liquids *and* gases; they encompass elements from multiple groups on the periodic table; and they show a wide range of chemical properties. Given this diversity, perhaps it is understandable that we tend to use defining criteria for non-metals that tell us what these elements *are not*, rather than what they *are*.

On the following pages:

C	Carbon	P	Phosphorus
N	Nitrogen	S	Sulfur
O	Oxygen	Se	Selenium

1 H																	2 He
3 Li	4 Be											5 B	6 C	7 N	8 O	9 F	10 Ne
11 Na	12 Mg											13 Al	14 Si	15 P	16 S	17 Cl	18 Ar
19 K	20 Ca	21 Sc	22 Ti	23 V	24 Cr	25 Mn	26 Fe	27 Co	28 Ni	29 Cu	30 Zn	31 Ga	32 Ge	33 As	34 Se	35 Br	36 Kr
37 Rb	38 Sr	39 Y	40 Zr	41 Nb	42 Mo	43 Tc	44 Ru	45 Rh	46 Pd	47 Ag	48 Cd	49 In	50 Sn	51 Sb	52 Te	53 I	54 Xe
55 Cs	56 Ba	57–71	72 Hf	73 Ta	74 W	75 Re	76 Os	77 Ir	78 Pt	79 Au	80 Hg	81 Tl	82 Pb	83 Bi	84 Po	85 At	86 Rn
87 Fr	88 Ra	89–103	104 Rf	105 Db	106 Sg	107 Bh	108 Hs	109 Mt	110 Ds	111 Rg	112 Cn	113 Nh	114 Fl	115 Mc	116 Lv	117 Ts	118 Og

57 La	58 Ce	59 Pr	60 Nd	61 Pm	62 Sm	63 Eu	64 Gd	65 Tb	66 Dy	67 Ho	68 Er	69 Tm	70 Yb	71 Lu
89 Ac	90 Th	91 Pa	92 U	93 Np	94 Pu	95 Am	96 Cm	97 Bk	98 Cf	99 Es	100 Fm	101 Md	102 No	103 Lr

Metal opposites

We typically think of the non-metals as poor conductors of heat and electricity, as elements that tend to either gain or share electrons during chemical reactions, that have relatively low melting and boiling points, and that are not malleable or ductile. By using these parameters, what we are really saying is that they possess many properties that are the opposite of metals. In this regard the classification makes sense, but there are problems with such flexibility. For example, although these general ideas commonly create a list of seventeen elements that we classify as non-metals (hydrogen, helium, nitrogen, oxygen, fluorine, neon, chlorine, argon, krypton, xenon, radon, bromine, carbon, phosphorus, sulfur, selenium and iodine), there is wiggle room. Selenium may be classified as a metalloid, and further subtle nuances also occur. In this book, as in many similar instances, several of the non-metals in that list of seventeen are extracted into their own collections (the halogens and the noble gases, for example) for separate discussion. It makes sense for them to be treated in that way because their similarities with members of their respective groups

⊛ *A mixture of gases, chiefly sulfur dioxide, billowing into the sky from a sulfur mine in East Java, Indonesia.*

would be lost and not highlighted if they were collected together in the much more general category of non-metals. Additionally, pulling hydrogen out as a single entity, unassociated with any other elements, best highlights its uniqueness.

Those considerations leave us with a list of six elements that we will treat as the quintessential non-metals: carbon, nitrogen, oxygen, phosphorus, sulfur and selenium.

◀ *Graphite and diamond are two allotropes of one important non-metal, carbon. Allotropes are different forms of a single element and can have very different properties.*

C Carbon

Chemical symbol	C
Atomic number	6
Atomic mass	12.011
Boiling point	(graphite) 3550 °C (6422 °F)
Melting point	(graphite) 3825 °C (6917 °F)

Is element number 6 the most important element on earth? One can construct a pretty convincing argument in favour of answering yes. As the basis of all of organic chemistry, and hence all chemistry of life, carbon is literally at the centre of the most important molecules known. Whether it is in DNA and chlorophyll, or amino acids and cellulose, plant and animal life is constructed around, and dependent on, molecules made from carbon atoms.

Ⓐ *Charcoal is a familiar manifestation of carbon that we may encounter in our everyday lives. It can be produced from the slow heating of wood in the absence of oxygen.*

Early days

Carbon can be considered as being one of the prehistoric elements, inasmuch as no single discoverer can be easily defined. As prehistoric man was playing around with fire, and inevitably charcoal, he was handling pure carbon. Lavoisier's original list of elements, published in 1789, included carbon, as did Dalton's list published in 1805. Between these two lists, Smithson Tennant proved in 1796 that diamond was made from carbon, since burning it produced only carbon dioxide.

Ⓐ *Organic chemistry is the chemistry of carbon. Carbon atoms form the backbone of a multitude of naturally occurring, vitally important compounds, such as cellulose and chlorophyll, found in plants.*

Electron
configuration: 2.4

Isotopic significance

As the fifteenth most abundant element on earth, carbon exists naturally as three isotopes, carbon-12, carbon-13 and carbon-14. Two of these have special significance in chemistry, and for very different reasons. Carbon-12 is used as the standard by which the masses of all other atoms are measured. Taking the mass of $^1/12$ of a carbon-12 atom as a standard, all atoms have masses expressed as multiples of that unit. Carbon-14 is radioactive, with a half-life of 5,730 years. By measuring the amount of carbon-14 remaining in dead plant or animal material, the age of that material can be calculated. The older the material, the less carbon-14 will remain. This radiocarbon dating is a standard tool for archaeologists, and the development of the process by Willard Libby (1908–1980) won him the Nobel Prize in Chemistry in 1960.

Fullerenes

With its unique ability to form four bonds with itself, and its two familiar allotropes of graphite and diamond, carbon truly is an extraordinary element. In the mid-1980s and into the 1990s, a further allotrope of carbon became known. In addition to the much more familiar diamond and graphite, a number of other, more elaborate, hollow three-dimensional arrangements of carbon atoms called fullerenes were prepared, first at Rice University in Texas, USA. Having been proposed by a number of scientists around the world prior to the 1980s, the first one produced was a soccer-ball-shaped structure composed of carbon atoms arranged in hexagonal and pentagonal formations. It is known as buckminsterfullerene, C_{60}. The fullerene family also includes tubular structures known as nanotubes, which are of particular interest in part for their ability to impart enhanced strength to materials that contain them.

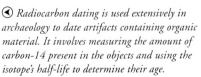

▶ *Crystallised buckminsterfullerene, C_{60}, one of the allotropic forms of elemental carbon.*

◀ *Radiocarbon dating is used extensively in archaeology to date artifacts containing organic material. It involves measuring the amount of carbon-14 present in the objects and using the isotope's half-life to determine their age.*

N Nitrogen

Chemical symbol	N
Atomic number	7
Atomic mass	14.007
Boiling point	−195.80 °C (−320.43 °F)
Melting point	−210 °C (−346 °F)

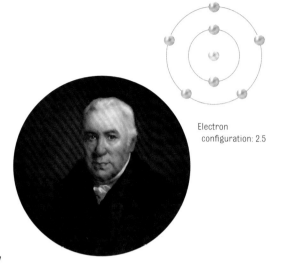

Electron
configuration: 2.5

Any element that makes up approximately 78 percent of the air must be pretty important, and element number 7 is certainly a significant one. Like oxygen, nitrogen forms a diatomic molecule in its elemental state. The N_2 molecule differs from the O_2 molecule in one significant way, though. While oxygen atoms are bonded to one another with a double covalent bond, the two nitrogen atoms in an N_2 molecule are bound together by a triple bond.

(A) *Scottish chemist Daniel Rutherford was a student of Joseph Black. In 1772, Rutherford was the first person to isolate nitrogen. He called it 'noxious air'.*

Noxious air

With so much of it floating around in the atmosphere, and an enormous amount of investigation of 'airs' (the collective name for various gases in the second half of the eighteenth century), nitrogen's relatively early discovery was inevitable. Several chemists came close, but the discovery is credited to Daniel Rutherford (1749–1819), a Scottish chemist. His experimentation essentially involved suffocating a mouse. The mouse was confined to a small container where it used up all of the oxygen. Rutherford realised that there was still 'an air' left in the container that would not support respiration, and since it caused the death of the mouse, he called it 'noxious' air; this was eventually superseded by the modern name at the end of the eighteenth century.

(▼) *The oxygen molecule is formed when a pair of oxygen atoms are covalently bonded with a double bond. The nitrogen atoms in N2, on the other hand, make a triple covalent bond.*

Oxygen
O_2

Nitrogen
N_2

Explosive bond

As a gas, diatomic nitrogen is basically inert. This is due mainly to the incredibly strong triple bond that two nitrogen atoms form in an N_2 molecule. The strong attraction that they have for one another means that nitrogen gas tends not to interact with many substances, but nitrogen's incredibly strong bond is also the key to its incredible power. Many compounds contain nitrogen atoms that are not combined with other nitrogen atoms, for example in trinitrotoluene, better known as the explosive TNT. TNT can be easily provoked into a reaction where the individual nitrogen atoms in the compounds are persuaded to come together and form N_2 gas. The incredible force by which the atoms are brought together to make the diatomic molecule releases a large amount of energy. When this process is repeated in a typical reaction trillions of times, the release of energy is colossal, and this is how nitrogen-based explosives work. This power is also harnessed in car airbags, which contain sodium azide, NaN_3. When detonated in a collision, NaN_3 also forms large amounts of N_2 extremely rapidly, causing the airbag to instantaneously inflate.

It is the instantaneous release of a controlled amount of nitrogen gas in a chemical reaction that allows a car airbag to inflate rapidly.

Nitrogen fixation

Nitrogen has a crucial role to play in biology in such essential compounds as amino acids, and plants need to be able to 'fix' nitrogen by taking relatively useless N_2 and converting it to useful compounds such as ammonia, NH_3. Nitrogen fixation can occur naturally when bacteria in the soil convert nitrogen for plant use, but many fertilisers such as ammonium nitrate (NH_4NO_3) are important agricultural chemicals, since they provide nitrogen in a usable form.

Arguably the most important application of nitrogen is in the manufacture of fertilisers and, hence, the production of food for the planet.

O Oxygen

Chemical symbol	O
Atomic number	8
Atomic mass	15.999
Boiling point	−182.96 °C (−297.33 °F)
Melting point	−218.79 °C (−361.82 °F)

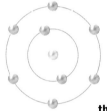

Electron configuration: 2.6

If its fellow non-metal element carbon is the very stuff of life, then the gaseous element just a couple of spots to the right on the periodic table isn't far behind in terms of its importance – it drives life. Without it, animals, including humans, could not survive, so its ubiquitous presence in the atmosphere is the very key to life on earth.

⊙ *As well as being touted as the discoverer of oxygen, Joseph Priestley was well known and highly regarded as a clergyman and educator.*

Who gets the credit?

In addition to making up 21 percent of the atmosphere of earth, oxygen is the third most abundant element in the universe as a whole. As such, and much like nitrogen, it was destined to be one of the elements that would be discovered early in the history of chemistry. The discovery (and discoverer) of oxygen is open to a little debate. The Swede Carl Wilhelm Scheele first identified the gas in 1772 by liberating it from a number of oxygen-containing compounds, but his findings were not published until a few years later. In the meantime, Englishman Joseph Priestley (1733–1804) identified oxygen via the decomposition of an oxide of mercury, and since he published his findings first, he is often awarded priority. Priestley experimented with the new gas by exposing both mice and himself to it. He is famously quoted as saying, 'The feeling of it to my lungs was not sensibly different from that of common air, but I fancied that my breast felt peculiarly light and easy for some time afterwards.' Depending on the source, Priestley, Scheele, or even both, are sometimes credited with the discovery of the first member of group 16.

'The feeling of it to my lungs was not sensibly different from that of common air, but I fancied that my breast felt peculiarly light and easy for some time afterwards.'

—Joseph Priestley, *Experiments and Observations on Different Kinds of Air*, 1775

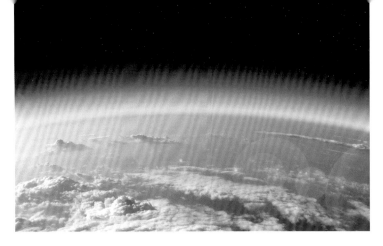

Approximately 21 percent of the air in earth's atmosphere is oxygen, the remainder being almost exclusively nitrogen, with small amounts of several other gases also present.

In nature and in industry

Because of its central role to respiration, it is easy to see why oxygen is so important, but the importance of element number 8 to life on earth goes way beyond that. As one of its allotropes, ozone (O_3), oxygen protects the earth from the sun's harmful ultraviolet rays. The depletion of the ozone layer around the earth by reaction with many chemicals, notably CFCs (see p. 195), has led to the banning of many such compounds. As a relatively soluble gas, oxygen is found in water systems, and helps to sustain a large amount of aquatic animal and plant life. Oxygen is a crucial substance in many industrial processes, not least of all as it supports combustion (burning). Whenever a situation requires the burning of a fuel, oxygen must be present, and in industrial settings its addition can help increase the temperatures at which things burn. In oxyacetylene welding, for example, ethene is burned in a stream of O_2 to produce an unusually hot flame that allows the metals literally to melt together.

Oxidation

Despite its vital role in life on earth, oxygen's ubiquitous presence in the atmosphere is not always welcome. As a reactive gas, over time oxygen has a tendency to react with just about anything that it comes into contact with. This is especially true of its reaction with metals, notably iron. Such a reaction, known generically as oxidation, may simply produce a relatively harmless oxide layer that tarnishes the surface of the metal – as it does when silver cutlery is exposed to air – or it may pose a more serious problem, leading to mechanical corrosion when iron rusts. Either way, huge amounts of money and man-hours are devoted to arresting the reaction of the most potent of all oxidisers, oxygen.

Rusting iron nails exhibit the characteristic reddish-brown hydrated iron(III) oxide coating that we associate with the corroding metal.

P Phosphorus

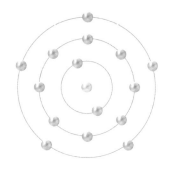

Electron configuration: 2.8.5

Chemical symbol	P
Atomic number	15
Atomic mass	30.974
Boiling point	(white) 280.50 °C (536.90 °F)
Melting point	(white) 44.15 °C (111.47 °F)

ⓥ *It has been suggested that Joseph Wright's famous painting of 1771,* The Alchymist in Search of the Philosopher's Stone Discovers Phosphorus, *refers to Hennig Brand's discovery of phosphorus in 1669.*

Phosphorus's frightening reputation as an element of chaos often precedes it, so it can be easy to overlook the crucial role that it plays in living cells. As an element of war, element number 15 has been responsible for a great deal of death and destruction. As an element of life, its role in the vital biological molecules ATP (adenosine triphosphate) and DNA means that we simply cannot survive without it.

The philosopher's stone

Phosphorus is one of the earliest elements whose discovery can be specifically attributed to an individual. Hennig Brand (1630–1710) was one of many alchemists of his time who were searching for the philosopher's stone. A legendary substance, the philosopher's stone was thought to possess a number of extraordinary powers that included the ability to deliver immortality and the chemical power to turn base metals such as mercury and lead into gold. The idea of the philosopher's stone spurred all kinds of astonishing, chemical wild-goose chases, and it was on one of these that Brand discovered phosphorus in 1669. By heating a vat of human urine, Brand had hoped ultimately to extract gold. What he got instead was a substance that glowed in air, and that he called *phosphorus* after the same Greek word, meaning 'bearer of light'.

Deep burn

Phosphorus is another of the non-metallic elements that can exist in a number of allotropic forms. The different forms are characterised by their colours, with white, red and black being three common types. It is the flammable and poisonous white form that has had the most devastating effects in times of war, as it has been used to create smoke screens and terrifying incendiary bombs. White phosphorus is known to cause deep second- and third-degree burns on victims, and is a devastating poison – the after-effects of a bombardment with white phosphorus include severe liver problems. As such, WP, as it is also known, has continued to enjoy a controversial reputation that walks a fine line between a legitimate offensive and defensive weapon, and that of an unacceptable agent of chemical warfare.

The devil's element

The incendiary nature of white phosphorus was harnessed by its use in the match industry in the late nineteenth century. However, how one views the success of that particular endeavour largely depends on perspective. The workers in match factories were subject to dreadful working conditions, including the horrible occupational disease 'phossy jaw'.

The United States used white phosphorus munitions against the Vietcong during the Vietnam War.

Caused once again by the nefarious WP that was used to make the matches, the condition created painful and disfiguring abscesses in the jawbone and a putrid-smelling pus. Without treatment, the disease could prove fatal. Given the turbulent history of element number 15, it is hardly surprising that the popular science writer and academic John Emsley wrote a book with the title, *The Shocking History of Phosphorus: A Biography of the Devil's Element* (2000).

The London match girls' strike of 1888 was an early piece of industrial action that protested the dangerous conditions encountered in match factories that used phosphorus.

S Sulfur

Chemical symbol	S
Atomic number	16
Atomic mass	32.06
Boiling point	444.60 °C (832.3 °F)
Melting point	115.21 °C (239.38 °F)

Sulfur's story is a powerful and complex mix of biblical myth, long-lost ancient history and putrid stink. Mentioned in the Bible multiple times under its pseudonym *brimstone*, sulfur was also known to the ancient Greeks. In modern chemical nomenclature the prefix *thio-* is used to denote the presence of the element, and 'thio' also has a theological connection, being taken from the Greek *Theos*, meaning 'God'.

Sulfur is one of the most ancient elements known to mankind, and that means its prehistoric discovery is not attributed to any one person. Its history as a recognisable element first emerges in alchemy, when the science of chemistry was transitioning from a philosophical pursuit to an experimental one. One of the earliest references to sulfur was in the alchemists' belief that it was part of the philosopher's stone (also see phosphorus, pp. 186–87). The philosopher's stone was, in its simplest manifestation, a mythical substance that, it was believed, could be used to turn base metals into gold.

In the twenty-first century, sulfur is far more likely to render itself in important compounds used in industry and beyond. Examples include sulfuric acid, one of the world's most important industrial chemicals; sulfur dioxide, which can be used as a preservative and bleaching agent; and in a far more pungent way, methanethiol, aka methyl mercaptan, which is used in various

◀ *Lumps of sulfur extracted, at great risk to the miners, from an active volcano in East Java, Indonesia. The sulfur is used to bleach sugar, make fertiliser and vulcanise rubber.*

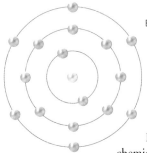

Electron configuration: 2.8.6

industrial settings including in the manufacture of pesticides. This chemical has the dubious distinction of being one of the foulest smelling on the planet. Such a malodorous distinction is typical of many sulfur compounds.

Allotropes

As a member of group 16, the bright yellow solid sits directly underneath oxygen on the periodic table and above the far less ubiquitous selenium. It is a reactive non-metal with a dizzying array of isotopes and, as a component of some amino acids, is one of the elements that are essential for life. It occurs naturally in a number of ways, including in compounds such as sulfides (those containing the S^{2-} ion) and as sulfates (SO_4^{2-}).

One of the more recognisable elements, sulfur is perhaps best known via one of its physical properties: that of the powdery, bright yellow substance that many encounter in the school chemistry lab. However, this is only one of many different forms (or allotropes) of the element. The powdered form has the common name 'flowers of sulfur', and is derived from another form of the element, the more crystalline orthorhombic sulfur.

Ⓐ One of the most visually distinctive elements, large mounds of sulfur can often be seen close to the point of mining.

What's in a name?

Over the years, the seemingly innocuous subject of an alternative spelling for sulfur has created quite a stink (!) of its own. If you are a user of British English, the name of this element is likely to raise some hackles. Even if the British spelling of 'sulphur' is the one that you are most familiar with, the organization charged with sorting out such disputes, the IUPAC, has long since made the 'f' spelling the official one. In 1992, even the quintessentially British Royal Society of Chemistry (RSC) gave up on the 'ph' spelling.

◄ Orthorhombic sulfur is the most common crystalline allotrope of sulfur because it is the most stable form below 96 °C (194 °F).

Se Selenium

Chemical symbol	Se
Atomic number	34
Atomic mass	78.971
Boiling point	685 °C (1265 °F)
Melting point	220.5 °C (428.90 °F)

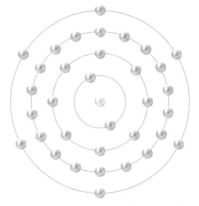

Electron configuration:
2.8.18.6

A somewhat obscure element, selenium is surprisingly one of the essential elements for humans. However, it is a delicate balance: with too little selenium, serious health issues can result, as cells find themselves unable to defend against disease; with too much selenium, there is the risk of a toxic reaction. That is to say nothing of the effect that selenium can have on your social life! Similar to the effect of tellurium, bad breath and body odour are symptoms of excess selenium.

Chronic halitosis is not the only way that selenium and tellurium are linked. When Jöns Jacob Berzelius discovered selenium in 1817, he named it after the Greek *selene*, meaning 'moon'. A strange choice, perhaps, but when one knows that tellurium had previously been named after the Latin *tellus*, meaning 'earth', his designation makes more sense, as it forever links the two chemically similar elements.

The delicate balance that selenium must find for good health in its role as an antioxidant can be illustrated by a couple of diverse examples: one where deficiencies caused deadly problems, and one where an excess of the element caused a curious observation among grazing animals.

◀ *One of the common allotropes formed by selenium is a grey-black crystalline solid. Another is a red powder.*

Too little

In the 1960s it was noticed that disproportionately large numbers of the population in certain regions of China were afflicted with debilitating heart conditions. Most badly affected were children and young women, who were dying from heart failure with worrying regularity. The common thread that ran through the areas where the higher occurrences were found was the selenium-deficient soil. The heart condition that was identified as being caused by the lack of element 34 was named Keshan disease after one of the areas of northeast China where the problem was most acute.

Too much

In a less profound situation, selenium can have a surprising effect on livestock. Once again, the chemical makeup of the soil is the key, but in these instances, rather than there being a lack of selenium in the soil, the exact opposite is true. Certain plants can take up large quantities of selenium, so that it becomes concentrated within them. The selenium-rich plants are then eaten by livestock, and the result, known in some places as the blind staggers, can be quite a sight to see. Cattle have been known to act as if they were drunk, unable to keep their balance and prone to falling over. The symptoms can be quite severe. One plant known to cause the problem, vetch, is also known as locoweed, from the Spanish *loco*, meaning 'crazy'.

⊙ *Selenium can accumulate in locoweed, causing problems for livestock that then consume the plant.*

Halogens

The halogens consist of the six elements in group 17 of the periodic table: fluorine, chlorine, bromine, iodine, astatine, and the newly minted (in 2016) tennessine. As volatile elements that are seeking one more electron in order to complete their valence p-subshells, they tend to react easily and form many compounds, and their collective name is derived from their willingness to do just that with positive metal ions: it means 'salt-forming'.

On the following pages:

F **Fluorine**   **I** **Iodine**

Cl **Chlorine**   **At** **Astatine**

Br **Bromine**

1 H																	2 He
3 Li	4 Be											5 B	6 C	7 N	8 O	9 F	10 Ne
11 Na	12 Mg											13 Al	14 Si	15 P	16 S	17 Cl	18 Ar
19 K	20 Ca	21 Sc	22 Ti	23 V	24 Cr	25 Mn	26 Fe	27 Co	28 Ni	29 Cu	30 Zn	31 Ga	32 Ge	33 As	34 Se	35 Br	36 Kr
37 Rb	38 Sr	39 Y	40 Zr	41 Nb	42 Mo	43 Tc	44 Ru	45 Rh	46 Pd	47 Ag	48 Cd	49 In	50 Sn	51 Sb	52 Te	53 I	54 Xe
55 Cs	56 Ba	57–71	72 Hf	73 Ta	74 W	75 Re	76 Os	77 Ir	78 Pt	79 Au	80 Hg	81 Tl	82 Pb	83 Bi	84 Po	85 At	86 Rn
87 Fr	88 Ra	89–103	104 Rf	105 Db	106 Sg	107 Bh	108 Hs	109 Mt	110 Ds	111 Rg	112 Cn	113 Nh	114 Fl	115 Mc	116 Lv	117 Ts	118 Og

57 La	58 Ce	59 Pr	60 Nd	61 Pm	62 Sm	63 Eu	64 Gd	65 Tb	66 Dy	67 Ho	68 Er	69 Tm	70 Yb	71 Lu
89 Ac	90 Th	91 Pa	92 U	93 Np	94 Pu	95 Am	96 Cm	97 Bk	98 Cf	99 Es	100 Fm	101 Md	102 No	103 Lr

Short-lived

Of these six, the first four halogens are by far the most important. The final two are little more than theoretical curiosities due to their radioactive nature, and the fact that no more than a handful of atoms of either have ever been produced. The atoms of astatine and tennessine that have been produced in laboratories are fleeting to say the least, with even the longest-lived isotope of astatine only enjoying a half-life of just over eight hours.

Salt-producing

In took just over 100 years, from 1774 to 1886, to discover the first four halogens. Chlorine came first, followed by iodine, bromine, and eventually fluorine. The designation 'salt-producing' came from the observation that the elements readily form salts with metals. The most common and ubiquitous of those salts is sodium chloride, but hundreds of such compounds can be made by combining a wide variety of metals with fluorine, chlorine, bromine, and iodine. In these compounds the halogens are in their ionic form with a charge of -1, and the collective name for these anions is 'halides', or more specifically, fluoride, chloride, bromide, and iodide.

The quest for electrons

As elements, the halogen atoms pair up with one another and exist as the diatomic molecules F_2, Cl_2, Br_2, and I_2. In this form, the elements exhibit increasingly high melting and boiling points, and as a result, their states at room temperature range from gases (fluorine and chlorine), through to a liquid (bromine), and finally to a solid (iodine). All are highly reactive, with fluorine and chlorine particularly so.

Much of the chemistry of the halogens revolves around their desire to gain an electron in order to achieve the more stable electron structure of a filled valence p-subshell. With an outer electronic configuration that sees five of the six spots in the p-subshell filled, the constant quest for electrons to fill the subshell and achieve relative stability makes the halogens excellent oxidising agents. (Oxidising agents are defined as substances that promote the oxidation of other substances, by accepting electrons.)

▶ *Fluorine, chlorine, bromine, and iodine samples at room temperature. F_2 and Cl_2 exist as gases, whereas Br_2 is a liquid that vaporises easily, and I_2 is a solid that sublimes.*

F Fluorine

Chemical symbol	F
Atomic number	9
Atomic mass	18.998
Boiling point	−188.11 °C (−306.62 °F)
Melting point	−219.67 °C (−363.41 °F)

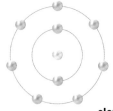

Electron configuration: 2.7

Sitting at the top of group 17, fluorine is another element with a nasty reputation for being cruel and unforgiving. Frankly, that reputation is well deserved. Throughout the history of the search for fluorine there were many casualties. Both as the highly reactive element and as the stunningly dangerous hydrofluoric acid (HF), element number 9 managed to poison, and ultimately kill, several prominent scientists of the nineteenth century.

Fluorine was finally tamed in 1886, when Frenchman Henri Moissan finally isolated it. It had been a long journey, and fluorine had wreaked plenty of destruction along the way, including inflicting illness on the great Humphry Davy and the Knox brothers from the Royal Irish Academy, and even killing Paulin Louyet (1818–50) and Jérôme Nicklès (1820–69). Bearing that in mind, Moissan's award of the 1906 Nobel Prize in Chemistry, in part, for 'his investigation and isolation of the element fluorine', was well deserved!

Long before fluorine was recognised as an element in its own right, it was known to be part of the important mineral fluorspar, CaF_2. Fluorspar had been used for centuries in the production of metals, since its addition helped the metals to become fluid. Knowing that, it is not surprising to learn that the name 'fluorine' comes from the Latin *fluere*, meaning 'to flow'.

◀ *French chemist Henri Moissan finally isolated fluorine in 1886.*

◀ *Moissan electrolysed KHF_2 (potassium bifluoride) dissolved in liquid HF in order to isolate fluorine. For this work, he was awarded the 1906 Nobel Prize in Chemistry.*

Notoriously reactive

Fluorine's quest for electrons is reflected in its being the most electronegative of all the elements known. Electronegativity is a measure of how likely an element is to attract electrons to itself, and this tendency makes fluorine highly reactive. As a pale yellow gas, fluorine will react violently with just about anything, with only a few of the aloof noble gases being spared. Not only is fluorine a notorious reactant when it comes into contact with inorganic materials, it is also found in a wide variety of organic compounds (those compounds made from carbon) – and things don't get much better in terms of reputation there.

CFCs

More trouble follows fluorine into the realm of organic chemistry, notably in the form of chlorofluorocarbons, or CFCs. In the latter part of the twentieth century, CFCs were widely used as refrigerants and propellants in aerosol cans. Their use eventually led to a public outcry when they were connected to the destruction of the ozone layer around the earth. Ozone has a crucial role to play in protecting the earth from the harmful ultraviolet rays of the sun, and CFCs were proved to be depleting this shield. Their use was phased out as part of an international agreement called the Montreal Protocol, first enforced in 1989.

◉ *The ubiquitous use of chlorofluorocarbons as aerosol propellants raised concerns over the destruction of the ozone layer, which ultimately led to the phasing-out of CFCs.*

Healthy teeth

On a more encouraging note, fluorine has had a positive role to play in at least one area of public health. As an addition to both the water supply and to toothpastes, fluoride ions help to reverse a process known as demineralization, which causes the destruction of tooth enamel.

◉ *Fluorine's (or more accurately, fluoride's) use in toothpastes and water supplies helps to strengthen tooth enamel and therefore reduce tooth decay.*

Cl Chlorine

Chemical symbol	Cl
Atomic number	17
Atomic mass	35.45
Boiling point	−34.04 °C (−29.27 °F)
Melting point	−101.5 °C (−150.7 °F)

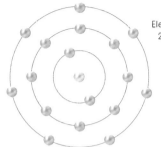

Electron configuration: 2.8.7

Sitting below fluorine and above bromine, chlorine is another element with a checkered past of both good and evil. As both the pure diatomic (where a pair of atoms are chemically bonded to one another to make a single molecule) element, Cl_2, and as a component of a wide-ranging collection of compounds, chlorine has inflicted terror and saved countless lives throughout recent history.

Discovered in 1774 by Swede Carl Wilhelm Scheele, chlorine had to wait until 1810 when Davy confirmed it as an element before its recognition was complete. Scheele had indeed made chlorine from a reaction between magansese(IV) oxide and hydrochloric acid (HCl), but he thought that he had produced another compound rather than an element.

Gas attack

As an agent of terror, the pure element was used as a chemical weapon in the First World War. In April 1915 in Ypres, France, German troops released over 150 tons of chlorine, representing the first use of a poisonous gas on the Western Front. The attack resulted in the death of approximately 5,000 French and Algerian troops. Horror stories surrounding the slow, but unrelenting cloud of distinctive yellow-

◀ *During the First World War, significant use of chemical weapons, including tear gas, mustard gas and phosgene, as well as chlorine, led to soldiers being issued with gas masks.*

green gas moving towards the Allies make for some of the most harrowing reminiscences of the Great War, especially when one considers the gruesome manner in which chlorine attacks. Horrible choking results, and mucous membranes in the throat and lungs, eyes and skin are attacked as the chlorine reacts with water to form hypochlorous and hydrochloric acids.

◀ *The chlorine-containing compound DDT was a popular ingredient of commercial insecticides in the 1960s, prior to its use being outlawed in the following decade.*

Environmental and health threat

Less dramatic in terms of immediate impact, but some would argue equally devastating in the long term, chlorine is found in several highly controversial and historically widely used compounds, including, for example, the notorious insecticide DDT (dichlorodi-phenyltrichloroethane). The inventor of DDT, Paul Müller (1899–1965), won the Nobel Prize for his work, largely because DDT had been so effective. However, in 1962, Rachel Carson's (1907–1964) book *Silent Spring* (1962) shed doubt upon the wisdom of such widespread use of chemical substances. At the time, there was no real research on the long-term effects of releasing such chemicals into the environment, and the book outlined many harmful effects of their use. Among other things, the book spurred the modern environmental movement, and precipitated a ban on the use of DDT for agricultural use in the United States in 1972. CFCs (chlorofluorocarbons, the controversial refrigerants and propellants) and THMs (trihalo-methanes, by-products of water chlorination) also have some gruesome stories of their own that illustrate why chlorine has a reputation as a harmful element.

Vital saviour

Conversely, the chlorination of water can be considered one of humanity's greatest chemistry-based achievements. The carefully controlled introduction of chlorine into the water supply might be the single most important piece of public health action over the last 120 years. In this role, chlorine's ability to oxidise (and therefore kill) many waterborne bacteria and viruses means that billions of people have been protected from waterborne diseases such as typhoid and cholera.

◀ *As a vital addition to drinking water, chlorine's oxidising ability has saved literally millions of lives around the world in the fight against waterborne diseases.*

Br Bromine

Chemical symbol	Br
Atomic number	35
Atomic mass	79.904
Boiling point	58.8 °C (137.8 °F)
Melting point	−7.2 °C (19.04 °F)

Bromine is one of only two of the 118 known elements (mercury being the other) that is a liquid at room temperature. It is also one of the few elements that exist as a diatomic molecule in their elemental state. The highly reactive orange-brown non-metal is prevalent on earth in the bromide salts found in seawater, and one of its common compounds has a mythical connection to the control of sexual urges.

B romine was first extracted from brine by Antoine Jérôme Balard (1802–76) in 1826. Carl Jacob Löwig (1803–90) had discovered the element a year earlier, but Balard published first. He isolated the element by reacting it with chlorine and recognising that the red liquid that was produced was something new and interesting. His original name for the element was 'muride', but the name was changed to bromine by the French Academy of Sciences – drawn from the Greek *bromos*, meaning 'stench' – in order for it to better match its recently found group 17 companions, chlorine and iodine.

Electron configuration: 2.8.18.7

Potassium bromide

Bromine is a nasty, corrosive, volatile element that can prove fatal to humans in very small doses. On the other hand, bromides (salts that are created when bromine atoms gain electrons, form negative ions and combine with positive metal atoms) have been used in various medicinal applications for centuries. Potassium bromide was first suggested as a treatment for syphilis but soon found favour as a drug used to control epilepsy and convulsions. Modern drugs such as phenobarbital have now

▶ *French chemist Antoine Jérôme Balard is usually credited with the discovery of bromine, but as is sometimes the case, an additional person is co-credited – in bromine's case, the German Carl Jacob Löwig.*

superseded that simple salt, but, interestingly, it persists in the treatment of epilepsy in dogs.

In this sedative role, potassium bromide was also promoted as a substance that could be used to suppress sexual urges, and it has a mythical reputation for being added to British soldiers' tea in the First World War for that purpose! It seems highly doubtful that this was in fact the case, since the more likely effect of the bromide would be to sedate the soldiers – not really a desirable effect among the men in the trenches.

Quelling other fires

In another, significantly different but nevertheless suppressant role, bromine is incorporated into chemicals that are used as fire-retardants. Large organobromine compounds can be used in the manufacture of furniture foams in order to increase safety. In so-called 'halon' fire extinguishers, bromine forms part of other, smaller organic molecules such as ($CBrF_3$) in Halon 1301. In both situations, bromine works via a complex mechanism that interferes with the chain reaction combustion process.

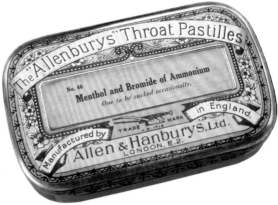

Bromides have been used in pharmaceutical preparations for centuries. These throat lozenges combined menthol with ammonium bromide, noted for its calming and hypnotic effects.

Pest control

Bromine's unpleasantness has been utilised in fumigants and pesticides. Historically, a number of organic compounds that contain bromine (known as organobromines) have been used in such applications, including bromomethane CH_3Br (aka methyl bromide) and 1,2-dibromo-3-chloropropane $CH_2BrCHBrCH_2Cl$ (aka DBCP). Despite their effectiveness, such compounds have fallen foul of increasingly tight regulations surrounding their impact on the environment, and like many similar halogen-based compounds, they have been largely phased out.

Bromotrifluoromethane, better known as Halon 1301, was developed at the request of the US Army to replace other, more toxic fire-suppressors.

I Iodine

Chemical symbol	I
Atomic number	53
Atomic mass	126.90
Boiling point	184.4 °C (363.92 °F)
Melting point	113.7 °C (236.66 °F)

⊙ *Solid iodine, which exists as blackish-grey crystals, will sublime at room temperature to produce the distinctive purple vapour that is often associated with the element.*

The largest and heaviest of the naturally occurring halogens, iodine is also the least reactive. Solid iodine exhibits a fascinating and unusual property at room temperature: it sublimes, turning directly from a solid to a gas with no liquid phase. It was the purple vapour produced as a result of this sublimation that suggested iodine's name, which derives from the Greek *iodes*, meaning 'violet'.

Like bromine, the family member directly above it on the periodic table, iodine is recovered from seawater, and its discovery came in 1811 when the French chemist Bernard Courtois (1777–1838) was experimenting with seaweed. Iodine is another element where the question of discovery proved a little contentious: the Englishman Humphry Davy also claimed iodine for his own, which proved to be a bit of a problem, since the French and the English were at war at the time.

Disinfectant

In another link to bromine, iodine has had, and continues to have, an important role to play in medicine. A traditional and familiar use for iodine is as an antiseptic. Despite being potentially damaging in large doses, the controlled application of iodine creates a very effective antiseptic barrier. As a tincture of iodine (an ethanol and water solution of the element and iodide ions), it is used topically on skin to disinfect around wounds or incisions. In this form, it leaves a familiar orange stain. A more modern version of a topical antiseptic, povidone-iodine, is used in a similar manner. It too contains elemental iodine, and although it generally has a higher percentage of the element present, the complex, organic chemical structure of povidone-iodine allows a more gradual and more effective release of iodine.

A balancing act

Iodine plays a crucial role in the human body and it needs to be regulated carefully to ensure correct body function. The thyroid gland in the neck is one organ where iodine accumulates, and the specific concentration of iodine there – either too high or too low – can lead to an overactive thyroid (hyperthyroidism) or an underactive thyroid (hypothyroidism). The latter may cause an abnormal swelling of the neck, known as a goiter. The balance is a delicate one, but most problems of this nature are brought about because of lack of iodine in the diet, and in order to

Electron configuration:
2.8.18.18.7

◀ Iodide ions, often in the form of sodium iodide, are one of the ingredients in iodine tincture (along with water, iodine and alcohol) and are added in order to help dissolve the elemental I$_2$.

combat this, iodised salt (common table salt mixed with various other salts that include iodine) was introduced as an effective way of supplementing people's diets.

Iodine-131

The most well-known of iodine's many isotopes is perhaps iodine-131. A radioactive isotope, it decays by releasing beta particles, and it is known to accumulate in the thyroid gland in humans. In such circumstances, thyroid cancers have been observed. As a product of many nuclear reactions, it posed a significant threat to human health in the wake of both the Chernobyl disaster in 1986 – where an explosion and fire at a Soviet nuclear power plant led to extensive nuclear pollution – and the more recent nuclear accident in Fukushima, Japan, in 2011 – where an earthquake and a resulting tsunami breached the seawall of a nuclear plant, causing a similar release of radioactive material.

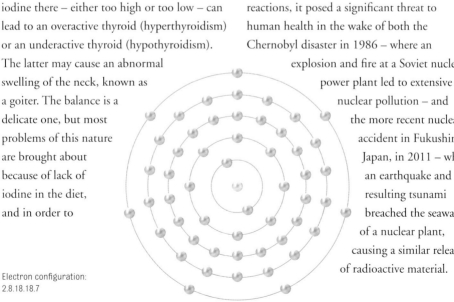

At   Astatine

Chemical symbol	At
Atomic number	85
Atomic mass	210 (longest-living isotope)
Boiling point	337 °C (638.6 °F)
Melting point	302 °C (575.6 °F)

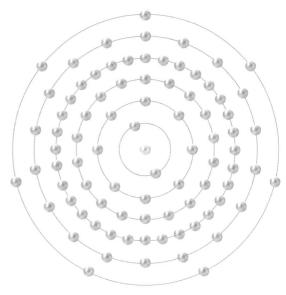

Electron configuration:
2.8.18.32.18.7

Astatine might be considered the poster child of elusive elements. Although it is one of the elements that occur naturally in the earth's crust, across the whole planet there is estimated to be only a few grams in total. Add the fact that all of astatine's isotopes are radioactive, most with very short half-lives, and it is hardly surprising that very little is known about the chemistry of element number 85.

Astatine's discovery story is an interesting one for a number of reasons. When Henry Moseley established the concept of ordering elements by their atomic number in 1913, it became apparent that seven elements were missing from the periodic table. (This story is the subject of Eric Scerri's 2013 book *A Tale of Seven Elements.*) One of these was the element with atomic number 85. This led several scientists to look for (and claim that they had found) the elusive element. Many of these claims were disproved, notably one made by Fred Allison

(see francium, pp. 24–25), who wanted to call element 85 'alabamine'. There were others too, and throughout the 1930s and '40s there were multiple names suggested for the element, and claims and counterclaims made for its discovery. Things were complicated even further by the start of the Second World War. Not only did it disrupt a lot of communication and general scientific progress, but American nuclear scientists had to concentrate on developing nuclear weapons as part of the Manhattan Project. It wasn't until after the war that a group in California was given credit for the element's discovery, and the period six halogen finally got its modern name.

The elusive element

Astatine's name is a good indicator of its elusiveness. The Greek *astatos* means 'unstable', and even though astatine is technically 'naturally occurring', with so little actually in existence, that classification is somewhat academic. In fact, it highlights an interesting fact about the elements as a whole, and an 'understanding' that exists in popular culture. Ask people who are casually interested in chemistry how many naturally occurring elements exist on earth, and the most likely answer that you will receive is ninety-two. The real answer is actually ninety-four, but when one considers the ultra-tiny amounts of elements like astatine, francium, technetium, promethium, neptunium and plutonium that exist naturally, there is some understandable debate and confusion about what 'naturally occurring' might reasonably mean. With so little in existence, very little is actually known about astatine's chemistry. The element's placement on the periodic table helps a little in that regard, and it is thought that much of its chemistry would likely be analogous with its closest halogen neighbour, iodine.

Bombarding bismuth

The Italian physicist Emilio Segrè, was part of the group at Berkeley that discovered astatine in 1940. The work involved bombarding bismuth-209 with alpha particles, and then analysing the radiation given off by the product of the collisions. Segrè's group concluded that the radiation was due to the electron capture of astatine atoms. However, because of the demands of the Manhattan Project and the war, it was not until 1947 that astatine was named. Astatine wasn't Segrè's only part in the discovery of the elements either. He was also a member of the team that discovered technetium in 1937.

◀ *Emilio Segrè's notable achievements go beyond the elements astatine and technetium. He also co-discovered the antiproton in 1955, which led to his sharing the 1959 Nobel Prize in Physics.*

Noble gases

All of the noble gases were discovered relatively late when compared to the bulk of the elements on the periodic table. One reason for this is their stability. If an element does not react with much, then it tends not to appear in many compounds that one might come across. Throw in the fact that the group 18 elements are colourless, odourless and tasteless gases, and you've got some pretty difficult-to-find elements.

On the following pages:

He	Helium	Kr	Krypton
Ne	Neon	Xe	Xenon
Ar	Argon	Rn	Radon

1 H																	2 He
3 Li	4 Be											5 B	6 C	7 N	8 O	9 F	10 Ne
11 Na	12 Mg											13 Al	14 Si	15 P	16 S	17 Cl	18 Ar
19 K	20 Ca	21 Sc	22 Ti	23 V	24 Cr	25 Mn	26 Fe	27 Co	28 Ni	29 Cu	30 Zn	31 Ga	32 Ge	33 As	34 Se	35 Br	36 Kr
37 Rb	38 Sr	39 Y	40 Zr	41 Nb	42 Mo	43 Tc	44 Ru	45 Rh	46 Pd	47 Ag	48 Cd	49 In	50 Sn	51 Sb	52 Te	53 I	54 Xe
55 Cs	56 Ba	57–71	72 Hf	73 Ta	74 W	75 Re	76 Os	77 Ir	78 Pt	79 Au	80 Hg	81 Tl	82 Pb	83 Bi	84 Po	85 At	86 Rn
87 Fr	88 Ra	89–103	104 Rf	105 Db	106 Sg	107 Bh	108 Hs	109 Mt	110 Ds	111 Rg	112 Cn	113 Nh	114 Fl	115 Mc	116 Lv	117 Ts	118 Og

		57 La	58 Ce	59 Pr	60 Nd	61 Pm	62 Sm	63 Eu	64 Gd	65 Tb	66 Dy	67 Ho	68 Er	69 Tm	70 Yb	71 Lu
		89 Ac	90 Th	91 Pa	92 U	93 Np	94 Pu	95 Am	96 Cm	97 Bk	98 Cf	99 Es	100 Fm	101 Md	102 No	103 Lr

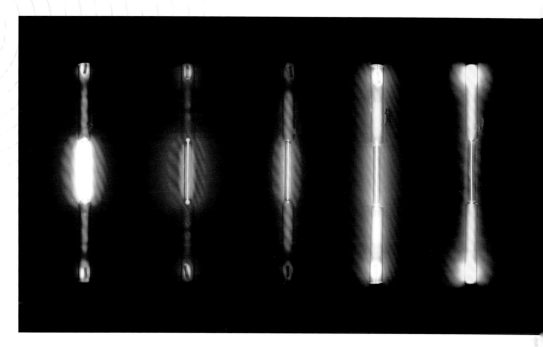

Domino effect

The discovery of argon came first, in 1894, but the discovery of the bulk of the noble gases was part of a domino effect. Morris William Travers (1872–1961) and William Ramsay (1852–1916) carried out increasingly sophisticated investigations on samples of air, and discovered krypton, neon and xenon within three months of one another between May and July 1898, a remarkably prolific and condensed run of filling in gaps in the periodic table.

Some may think of the noble gases as a bit boring, and for many years their alternative collective name, the *inert* (meaning 'unreactive') gases, was an appropriate designation. It took well over half a century after their discovery before the first compound of any of them was synthesised.

▲ *Discharge tubes filled with some of the noble gases – helium, neon, argon, krypton and xenon – emit bright, coloured light as the elements' electrons are excited by high voltages.*

Bright lights and cityscapes

Perhaps best known for their application in what are often referred to generically as 'neon' lights, the ability of many of the noble gases to emit vivid colours when exposed to high voltages is due to their electrons being excited to higher energy states, and then releasing that energy as they return to their ground (unexcited) state. Each element has a unique coloured fingerprint known as its spectrum, and the noble gases are particularly adept at producing the familiar city nightscapes.

He Helium

Electron
configuration: 2

Chemical symbol	He
Atomic number	2
Atomic mass	4.0026
Boiling point	−268.92 °C (−452.07 °F)
Melting point	−272.20 °C (−458 °F)

Helium is the second most abundant element in the universe, but there is precious little of it on earth. How can this be? The clue to its whereabouts is given away by element number two's name, which is derived from the Greek *helios*, meaning 'sun'. The sun is largely a ball of burning hydrogen gas, and helium is a product of the fusion of two hydrogen atoms.

On earth, the uranium mineral uraninite (UO_2) proved to be an unlikely source of helium gas. With the observation, made during a total eclipse of the sun, of a previously unknown spectral line in sunlight, astronomers Pierre Janssen (1824–1907) and Norman Lockyer (1836–1920) concluded that the sun must contain an element that had not yet been identified. William Ramsay matched the data from the sunlight with data that he collected from a gas that was liberated when uraninite reacted with acid. Two scientists in Sweden, Per Teodor Cleve and Nils Abraham Langlet (1868–1936), replicated Ramsay's work almost simultaneously, and sources will often credit both parties with the discovery.

Inert

As a noble gas, helium is pretty typical of group 18 in terms of its lack of reactivity. It has very tiny atoms and as such its negative electrons are very close to its positive nucleus, making the attraction between the two strong. This leads to the highest first ionization energy (the energy required to remove an electron) of all the elements, and means that helium is generally resistant to chemical reactions.

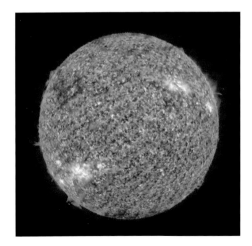

◀ *The sun is a star that fuses hydrogen nuclei together to produce helium. With that fusion comes the release of huge amounts of energy.*

Going up

As the second lightest element and as a gas, helium has found a number of uses in balloon technology. Ranging from airships to weather balloons and the more frivolous party balloons, helium's prevalent use in these applications, along with some changes in government policy in the United States, recently created some panic over a helium shortage. In the 1920s, the US government established the National Helium Reserve. Originally set up to ensure a reliable source of helium for military and space exploration (helium can be used as a coolant), the programme was abandoned in 1996, but not before huge reserves of the gas were released for sale. This sudden and massive influx caused some wild fluctuations in prices, and eventually distorted the market sufficiently to remove significant competition; ultimately, prices were driven up. This was a very big problem for science, since so many experiments rely upon liquid helium at a temperature of −269 °C (−452.2 °F), to provide the ultra-cold conditions often required for investigation at the atomic level. Some of the fear was dispelled when, in June 2016, a potentially massive new source of helium gas was discovered in Tanzania.

◀ *Helium gas is less dense than air, so a balloon that contains helium will rise. A popular application is in helium-filled party balloons.*

▼ *The USS* Macon, *a helium-filled airship, flying over New York City in 1933. It acted as a 'flying aircraft carrier' that smaller aircraft could be launched from.*

Ne Neon

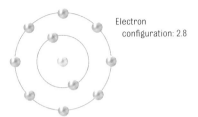

Electron
configuration: 2.8

Chemical symbol	Ne
Atomic number	10
Atomic mass	20.180
Boiling point	−246.05 °C (−410.88 °F)
Melting point	−248.59 °C (−415.46 °F)

Like its other family members, neon is inert and relatively uncommon (it is only the eighty-second most abundant element on earth), but it does have some important and well-known uses. 'Neon' lights are how most people will be familiar with the element, but such lights are seldom produced by neon alone. In other applications, neon also finds use as a low-temperature refrigerant, with a boiling point of around −246 °C (−411 °F).

Seek and ye shall find

With argon (with an atomic weight of approximately 40) and helium (with an atomic weight of approximately 4) already discovered, Ramsay and Travers went looking for a gas that they thought would have a mass somewhere between the two, and that we now realise would be neon. In actual fact, while seeking neon they ended up discovering krypton first in May 1898. However, they didn't have to wait long to discover the member of group 18 that they were originally seeking. They finally extracted element number 10 via the fractional distillation of a sample of argon in 1898. Interestingly, things haven't changed much since then. Neon is still extracted from the fractional distillation of liquid air. The process employs a more sophisticated apparatus than that used by the original discoverers, but is still based on the same physical principles.

◄ *The dazzling neon lights of a Las Vegas casino. The characteristic red glow is now synonymous with the term 'neon lights'.*

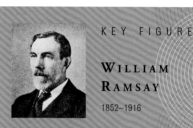

(A) *The unique spectrum of neon gas shows the prominence of lines in the orange-red part of the spectrum, which gives neon lights their distinctive colour.*

Crimson blaze

The name given to the element was derived from the Greek *neos*, meaning 'new', and was originally suggested in a slightly different form, *novum*, by Ramsay's son, Willie. With a nod to the future use of the element, Travers wrote of the spectrum that was observed in the lightest fraction of the distilled air: 'The blaze of crimson light from the tube told its own story, and it was a sight to dwell upon and never to forget.' He could not possibly have imagined the future prolific use of the element in neon lights, but his words were prophetic. Neon lights are now a familiar sight in cities all over the world, though it is only those that emit a bright red light that are likely to be utilising the element in its purest form. Different combinations of gases generate other colours; for example, xenon and mercury vapour produce vivid blue-greens.

By any standards, William Ramsay was an extraordinary figure when it comes to the discovery of the elements. He, along with Lord Rayleigh and William Travers, managed to isolate five of the seven group 18 elements over a period of approximately four years at the end of the nineteenth century. A Scotsman, Ramsay basically 'invented' group 18 via his discoveries, as the quotation that accompanied his 1904 Nobel Prize in Chemistry suggests: 'in recognition of his services in the discovery of the inert gaseous elements in air, and his determination of their place in the periodic system.'

Stable isotopes

Neon has three isotopes that occur naturally – neon-20, neon-21 and neon-22, with neon-20 being by far the most abundant. The chemical inertness of all of these is thought to be almost complete. Like helium, neon atoms have extremely high first ionization energies, and as such, they are resistant to reaction with all known substances. The unwillingness of the isotopes to react chemically is matched by the stability of their nuclei, none of which show any radioactive behaviour.

Ar Argon

Chemical symbol	Ar
Atomic number	18
Atomic mass	39.948
Boiling point	−185.85 °C (−302.53 °F)
Melting point	−189.34 °C (−308.81 °F)

Another colourless, odourless and tasteless gas, argon is certainly representative of its group 18 family members. However, argon is relatively plentiful; indeed, it is the third most abundant gaseous element (behind nitrogen and oxygen) in the atmosphere. It only amounts to approximately 1 percent of the atmosphere as a whole, but even that low percentage is over 500 times greater than the next most abundant group 18 element, neon.

(▲) *Lord Rayleigh, co-discoverer of argon with William Ramsay, working in his laboratory.*

Because of its relative abundance, argon proved to be the easiest of the noble gases to find. It was therefore the first to be discovered, and argon's discovery is a colossally important one in the bigger story of the evolution of the periodic table.

A whole new group

It all started with Henry Cavendish in the late eighteenth century when he was experimenting on air. He noticed that a tiny fraction of the air never reacted during his experiments, but, perhaps because the other gases that he was investigating distracted him, argon remained undiscovered. One hundred years later, Lord Rayleigh (John William Strutt, 1842–1919)

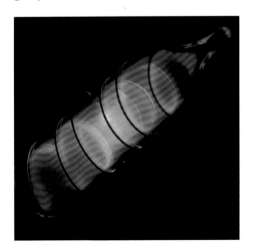

(◄) *An argon discharge tube, showing the characteristic purple glow that is associated with the gas.*

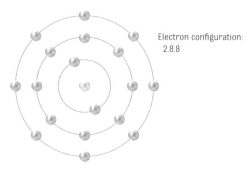

Electron configuration:
2.8.8

Non-reactive atmosphere

Most of argon's uses are based upon its inertness, and the fact that it cannot be provoked into reaction no matter how extreme the conditions. As such, it is used in a number of applications where a non-reactive atmosphere is required, such as in electric lights and fluorescent tubes. It is also used in the welding of aluminium, where the argon protects the metal from coming into contact with oxygen and therefore prevents unwanted oxidation reactions from occurring.

was experimenting with nitrogen. Rayleigh discovered that a number of the samples of nitrogen that he took from air were heavier and more dense than the samples that he obtained from sources that did not originate from air. Rayleigh had a number of theories as to why this was, but it took collaboration with William Ramsay to finally solve the mystery. By examining the spectrum of the gas isolated from the air samples, the two concluded that in addition to nitrogen, there was a previously undiscovered element present. In 1894, Ramsay wrote to Rayleigh saying, 'Has it occurred to you that there is room for gaseous elements at the end of the first column of the periodic table?' Essentially, Ramsay was suggesting that the new gas (which was named after the Greek *argos*, meaning 'lazy' or 'idle') could be part of a whole new group of elements that Mendeleev's early periodic table did not include. As such, it might be argued that the most important contribution that argon has ever made to chemistry is the fact that it spurred the search for a whole new group of previously unconsidered elements.

(▶) *Argon can be used as 'a shielding gas' in welding, where the inert atmosphere that it creates prevents water vapour and oxygen gas from interfering with the welding process.*

Kr Krypton

Chemical symbol	Kr
Atomic number	36
Atomic mass	83.798
Boiling point	−153.42 °C (−244.15 °F)
Melting point	−157.37 °C (−251.27 °F)

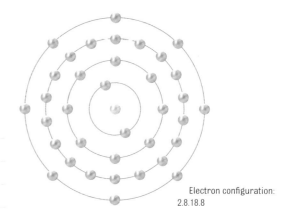

Electron configuration:
2.8.18.8

⊙ *William Ramsay, the driving force behind the discovery of the noble gases, shown here in a caricature that appeared in* Vanity Fair *magazine in 1908.*

Krypton exhibits the basic physical properties that one would expect of a quintessential member of group 18. Like the other noble gases, because of its inertness and relative lack of abundance – only very small amounts of the element are present as a gas in the atmosphere – krypton was not easy to find. This is reflected in its name, which is taken from the Greek *kryptos*, meaning 'hidden'.

In fact, krypton's discovery was a bit of an accident altogether. With argon and helium already identified as new members of the newest group, Ramsay and Travers went in search of another element that they thought might sit between those two elements. With the atomic masses of the two new gases established as approximately 4 and 40 respectively, they thought that they should look for a member of the group that had a mass of about 20. Their hunch was right, but when they went hunting for what would eventually turn out to be neon, rather than finding a lighter gas than argon, they came across an even heavier one in the process. Once again isolated through the distillation of liquid air, and once again pinpointed through a new line in the spectrum (this time green), another noble gas was identified, this time with an atomic mass between those of bromine and rubidium. This placed the new element perfectly in group 18, and in May 1898, krypton was 'born'.

The length of a metre

Krypton's uses are very similar to those of the other noble gases; that is, it is used in lighting applications and in places where inert atmospheres are required. But krypton also has a special place in the history of the International System of Units, or SI. The base unit for length as defined by the SI is the metre. Like all such base units, the base quantity must be defined in a very specific way. Today, the metre is defined as the distance travelled by light in $^1/_{299,792,458}$ of a second, but it has been characterised in several other ways in the past. One such definition involved a particular isotope of krypton: krypton-86. Between 1960 and 1983, the SI base unit of length was defined as: '1,650,763.73 wavelengths of the orange-red emission line in the electromagnetic spectrum

Ⓐ *The international prototype metre bar, the original standard of length prior to 1960, when the use of krypton-86 replaced it.*

of the krypton-86 atom in a vacuum.' Krypton has a dizzying array of isotopes, most radioactive, which have masses ranging in the high 60s all the way through to those with masses of over 100. The isotopes have an equally wide range of radioactive properties as well, but krypton-86 is very stable. It was this stability that helped cement its use in the definition of the metre.

Ⓟ *Interference rings produced by a Fabry–Pérot interferometer. On the right is the pattern produced by krypton-86, which was the basis for the determination of the SI base unit of length.*

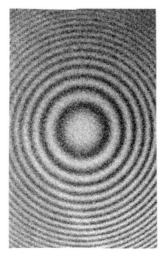 

Xe Xenon

Chemical symbol	Xe
Atomic number	54
Atomic mass	131.29
Boiling point	−108.10 °C (−162.58 °F)
Melting point	−111.75 °C (−169.15 °F)

Element number 54 occupies the final position in period 5. Like the other members of group 18, xenon is a colourless and odourless gas, and that means it is far from easy to find. The ability of xenon to remain hidden from detection (and therefore discovery) for so long contributed to its name, which is taken from the Greek *xenos*, meaning 'stranger'.

The final gas

With argon, neon, krypton and helium all in the bag, xenon was the final noble gas waiting to be discovered. In July 1898, Ramsay and Travers continued their work on the distillation of liquid air, this time with new equipment that had been given to them by the German/British chemist Ludwig Mond (1839–1909). After continually extracting fractions from a sample of krypton, they finally managed to isolate element number 54.

Late to the periodic party

Much like the other noble gases, xenon's chemistry is limited when compared to many other elements, but is important simply for the fact that it helped to shatter the perceived (and at the time, real) aloofness of the group 18 elements. In 1962, British-born chemist Neil Bartlett (1932–2008) made the first compound of any of the noble gases. Bartlett synthesised a compound of xenon, platinum and fluorine, by reacting platinum hexafluoride with xenon. The formation of the first compound to contain a noble gas was a seminal moment, since it opened up a whole new branch of chemistry. Bartlett's work

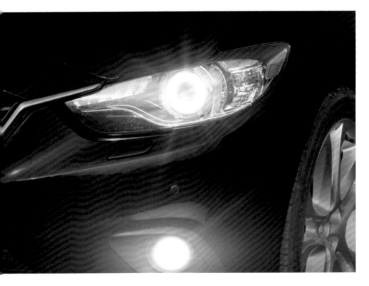

◀ *Longer-lasting, brighter, and capable of producing more intense light than conventional headlights, xenon lighting is now being used in some high-end vehicles.*

led to more compounds of xenon with fluorine and oxygen, such as XeF_2, XeF_4, XeO_2F_2, XeO_3, XeO_2 and XeF_6. Other noble-gas compounds have been made, notably using krypton, but xenon is by far the most interesting of the noble gases in terms of the compounds that it can form. Xenon compounds find use as strong oxidising agents and as sources of fluorine, although the use of the oxides is fraught with danger since they are highly unstable and explosive.

Ion propulsion

Xenon as an element has been used as a general anaesthetic, as an ion engine by NASA for spacecraft propulsion, and in a more familiar role associated with the noble gases, as a source of light. Here, the movement of electrons within excited xenon atoms emits a characteristic blue colour. In ion engines,

⌃ *An ion thrust engine in action. Accelerated ions produce the thrust.*

the propellant (in this case xenon gas) is ionised (has electrons removed) and then the resultant positively charged species are accelerated to speeds of tens of thousands of miles per hour using an electrical field. In turn, this produces thrust. Xenon has a host of chemical and physical properties that make it suitable for use in such engines utilised by some spacecraft: it is inert, so will not cause corrosion; as a gas, it can be compressed, so a large quantity of it can be stored in a very small space; it has a relatively low ionization energy to allow for easy ionization; and it has a high atomic mass, which creates a significant thrust.

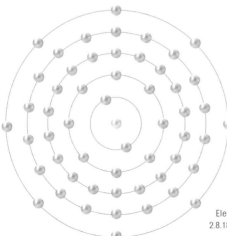

Electron configuration:
2.8.18.18.8

215

Rn Radon

Chemical symbol	Rn
Atomic number	86
Atomic mass	222 (longest-living isotope)
Boiling point	−61.70 °C (−79.10 °F)
Melting point	−71 °C (−96 °F)

Until recent discovery and confirmation of element 118 (with the placeholder name Uuo and the proposed name oganesson), radon was officially the heaviest and most dangerous of the noble gases. Although no longer the heaviest, because of its potent radioactivity and the fact that oganesson is set to remain not much more than a laboratory-based curiosity, radon's reputation as the most fearsome member of group 18 is likely to continue well into the future.

Electron configuration:
2.8.18.32.18.8

Not unlike several other elements, radon has a complicated history of discovery. However, even among that particularly well-established trend, few elements have enjoyed quite the array of different names and created the level of confusion that radon has.

Causing confusion

Right at the end of the nineteenth century, the understanding of the phenomenon that we now know as radiation was in its infancy. One of the consequences of this limited understanding was that radon's birth as an element was a confusing one. Originally recognised as a gas that was given off from the element radium, it was given the literal name 'radium emanation'. Things got very muddled, very quickly, when similar 'emanations' were observed from the elements thorium and actinium, and were given names such as thoron and action, as well as thorium emanation and actinium emanation. When Friedrich Dorn (1848–1916) was credited with the official discovery of element number 86 in 1900, there was still a great deal of confusion surrounding what it should be called. Things were complicated even further by the fact that scientists were encountering isotopes of elements that were already known, and, as isotopes had not yet been conceived, they thought that these were 'new' elements. All this, combined with the fact that these atoms were all radioactive

The room for preparing radon at the Radium Institute (now the Curie Institute) in Paris, France. The institute was originally founded as a laboratory for Marie Curie in 1909.

Health risk

Radon's appearance in modern society is also not without controversy. The radioactive nature of element number 86 is immortalised in its name, which comes from element number 88, radium, which in turn comes from the Latin *radius*, meaning 'ray'. During the final two decades of the twentieth century, radon gas was recognised as a potentially serious health risk. Naturally occurring radon was found to have accumulated in certain locations, and in 1988 the International Agency for Research on Cancer declared it a human carcinogen. As part of its natural decay pattern, radon produces other dangerous isotopes such as lead-210, which have long half-lives and will persist in the body for a long time, causing serious health issues.

with short half-lives, meant that confusion was high! In the early part of the twentieth century, many periodic tables carried the symbol Em, for emanation, and the king of the noble gases, William Ramsay, had also proposed the name 'niton' for number 86. It was not until the mid-1920s that radon became the accepted name, and that was largely due to the fact that it was the name of the isotope that had the longest half-life.

Bulbs filled with radon were once offered for sale so that people could produce their own radon-infused water at home. At one time, such water was considered a health tonic.

Glossary

Adsorbed: The process of particles collecting on the surface of a solid (often a metal)

Alkenes: A family of hydrocarbons that contain a carbon-to-carbon double bond, and that have the general formula C_nH_{2n} (where n is an integer)

Allotrope: Alternative forms of the same element, distinguished by differing structures and properties, despite being made up of identical atoms (e.g., carbon in the form of diamond and graphite)

Amu: The atomic mass unit, equal to $^1/_{12}$ of the mass of a C-12 atom, i.e., 1.66×10^{-27} kg

Anion: A negatively charged ion, created by the gain of electrons

Atomic number: Denotes the number of protons in the atoms of any given element

Atomic orbital: Three-dimensional areas of space in an atom which define where an electron is most likely to be found

Atomic weight: The weighted average mass of an atom in amu, or the weighted average mass of 1 mole of atoms in grams

Cation: A positively charged ion, created by the loss of electrons

Complementary colours: Colours that sit directly opposite one another on a colour wheel, and that when combined produce a greyscale colour

Complex ion: An ion formed by the combination of smaller, simpler ions or molecules, e.g., Cu^{2+} and H_2O to give $[Cu(H_2O)_6]^{2+}$

Covalent bond: A shared pair of electrons between atoms, which joins the atoms together with a strong attraction. Often found in compounds made between non-metals, and denoted by a line drawn between the atom's chemical symbols

Critical mass: The smallest amount of fissile material needed for a sustained nuclear chain reaction

D-orbital: One type (along with s, p, and f) of atomic orbital

Daughter nuclides: A product of the nuclear decay of another nuclide, which may itself decay further

Diatomic: Literally, 'two atoms'. A small molecule that contains only two atoms, like nitrogen (N_2), oxygen (O_2), hydrogen (H_2) and the halogens (F_2, Cl_2, Br_2, I_2)

Eka- (prefix): Refers to the Sanskrit word for 'one', which Mendeleev used to describe missing elements on the periodic table that were 'one' space below a known element. For example, eka-aluminium was ultimately named gallium

Electrolysis: The process of using electricity to force otherwise nonspontaneous redox reactions to occur

Electron: A subatomic particle with a negative charge, found outside of the atom's nucleus in orbitals

Electronic configuration: The specific arrangement of the electrons within any given atom that gives the atom its chemical properties

Enrichment: The process of increasing the percentage of U-235 in a sample of uranium, in order to make it suitable for use in nuclear chain reactions

Essential (element): An element required by an organism for healthy growth and development

Half-life: The time taken for half of the atoms of a radioactive nuclide to decay

Ion: A charged particle, created by either the loss of electrons to become positive (cation), or the gain of electrons to become negative (anion)

Isotope: Atoms of the same element (with the same number of protons) that differ only in the number of neutrons present

IUPAC: International Union of Pure and Applied Chemistry, the organization that determines the rules regarding chemical nomenclature and atomic weights

Lanthanide contraction: Used to describe the larger-than-expected decrease in ionic radii of the lanthanoid elements. The effect also causes sixth-period transition elements to be smaller than expected

Manhattan Project: US government-led project, supported by the UK and Canadian governments, that researched and developed nuclear weapons in the 1940s. It helped usher in the Nuclear Age, and led to the extension of the periodic table beyond the naturally occurring elements

Metal: Elements that are characterised by their ability to conduct electricity and heat very well, and their tendency to be lustrous, malleable and ductile. Most elements are classified as metals

Metastable: A state that persists for a finite time, despite there being an alternative, lower energy state that will ultimately be reached

Mole: SI (see entry below) unit for the amount of substance. It is equal to the number of atoms in exactly 12 g of C-12. Also known as Avogadro's number, it has a value of 6.02×10^{23}

Neutron: A subatomic particle with a neutral charge that resides in the nucleus

Nucleus: The high-density centre of the atom, which is composed of protons and neutrons, and where virtually all of the mass of any atom is concentrated

Organometallic structures: Compounds consisting of metals bound to organic (carbon-containing) groups

Oxidation number or oxidation state: A system that assigns charges to atoms within any compound. It assumes that the compound is either ionic (in which case the charges are real), or, if the compound is covalent, it is the charge that the atoms would take on, if the compound were ionic

Oxidising agent: A substance that promotes oxidation, usually by removing electrons from the species that it is oxidising

Pathological science: Scientific research or theories that have proven to be false but which have persisted among some small groups who are tricked into reporting false results as fact

Phosphorescence: A process in which energy absorbed by a substance is released relatively slowly in the form of light

Phosphors: Substances that exhibit phosphorescence

Photon: A 'packet' of energy associated with electromagnetic radiation

Proton: A subatomic particle with a positive charge that resides in the nucleus

Red Book: One of the IUPAC's 'coloured books' that give definitive, official statements and rules regarding nomenclature conventions. The 'Red Book' deals with inorganic nomenclature

Redox reaction: A chemical reaction that involves the transfer of electrons from one species to another, thus changing the oxidation numbers of the reacting species

Reduced: A species is said to be reduced when it gains electrons and its oxidation number is lowered

Reducing agent: A substance that promotes reduction, usually by supplying electrons to the species that it is reducing

SI: A universal system of units used in science to create unambiguous quantities and measurements

Sublimation: A change of state directly from solid to gas, without passing through the liquid phase

Sulfate ions: Anions made up of sulfur and oxygen atoms that have the formula SO_4^{2-}

Index

A

abrasives, 137

acids, 11

actinium, 166–67

actinoids, 164–77

aircraft, 42–43, 44, 84, 103

alkali metals, 12–25

alkaline earth metals, 26–39

Allison, Fred, 24–25, 202

aluminium, 42–43, 102–3, 109, 211

anti-cancer drugs, 95, 97, 166–67

antimony, 121, 126–27

aqua regia, 90

Arfvedson, Johan August, 14

argon, 210–11

arsenic, 124 25

astatine, 193, 202–3

atomic bombs. See nuclear
weapons

atomic clocks, 22–23

atomic mass, 69

Auer von Welsbach, Carl,
138–39, 160

automotive industry,
47, 48, 75, 92, 95, 137, 183

B

Babbitt metals, 127

Balard, Antoine-Jérôme, 198

balloons, 207

banknotes, 147, 159

barium, 26–27, 36–37, 49, 135

Bartlett, Neil, 214–15

bases, 27

batteries, 15, 61, 113

Becquerel, Henri, 172

beer, 55

Berg, Otto, 71

beryllium, 26–27, 28–29

Berzelius, Jöns Jacob,
120, 136, 168, 190

biology

  animals, 59, 190–91

  human, 17, 19, 31, 32–33, 47, 52,
  59, 128, 190–91, 201

  plants, 19, 31, 147, 183, 191

  See also toxicity

bismuth, 114–15

blood, 32–33, 52, 59

bones, 34, 80–81

boron, 118–19, 121

Bose–Einstein
  condensates (BECs), 21

Boyle, Robert, 10

Brand, Hennig, 186–87

bromine, 198–99

bronze, 108

Bunsen, Robert, 20, 22

Bury, Charles R., 40

C

Cade, John, 14

cadmium, 80–81

calcium, 26–27, 32–33

camera lenses, 123, 135

cancer, 95, 97, 166–67, 217

capacitors, 85

carbon, 83, 87, 180–81

catalysts, 41, 47, 72–73,
  74–75, 89, 95, 99, 163

catalytic converters, 75, 95, 137

Cavendish, Henry, 10–11, 210

ceramics, 64

cerium, 136–37

caesium, 12–13, 22–23

CFCs (chlorofluorocarbons),
  195

Chadwick, James, 29

chemical weapons,
  65, 187, 196–97

Chenevix, Richard, 76

Chernobyl, 23, 35, 201

chlorine, 193, 196–97

chromium, 48–49

Cleve, Per Teodor, 154, 158, 206

cobalt, 54–55, 145

coins, 56, 58, 67, 94, 96

cold fusion, 77

Coltan, 85

complex ions, 41

copper, 58–59

corrosion resistance,
  44, 45, 48, 61, 74, 83, 84,
  92, 96, 103, 108–9

cosmetics, 126–27

Cotton, Albert, 88–89

Courtois, Bernard, 200

Crawford, Adair, 34

Crookes, William, 110, 146

cupronickel, 58

Curie, Marie & Pierre,
  38, 130, 176

curium, 176–77

D

dating techniques, 135, 144, 181

Davy, Humphry, 16, 18, 34,
  71, 119, 120, 194, 196, 200

DDT (dichlorodiphenyl-
  trichloroethane), 197

Del Rio, Andrés Manuel, 46

Delafontaine, Marc, 151, 154–55

Deville, Henri Sainte-Claire, 102

diamonds, 63, 87, 180

didymium, 139

Disappearing Spoon, The, 105

doping, 125, 141, 155, 157

dyes, 124

dysprosium, 152–53

E

Ehrlich, Paul, 124

electrical conductors,
59, 78, 85, 97. *See also*
semi-conductors

electronic components,
85, 96, 97, 121, 133

Elinvar, 57

environmental pollution, 80–81,
98–99, 109, 137, 197, 199

eponymous elements, 144–45

erbium, 150–51, 156–57

Ertl, Gerhard, 95

europium, 146–47

F

ferrocerium, 136–37

fertilisers, 19, 183

Fiestaware, 173

fire safety uses, 115, 199

fireworks, 27, 35, 37

fission, nuclear, 172–73

Fleischmann, Martin, 77

Flint water crisis, 113

flints, 135, 136

fluorine, 193, 194–95

fool's gold, 53

Ford, Henry, 47

francium, 12–13, 24–25

Fukushima, 23, 35, 201

fullerenes, 181

G

Gadolin, Johan, 62, 148

gadolinium, 148–49, 158

Gahn, Johan Gottlieb, 50

gallium, 104–5, 107, 121

galvanised steel, 61

gemstones, synthetic, 63

germanium, 122–23

gold, 90, 96–97, 128

golf clubs, 44

gorillas, 85

green algae, 135

groups in periodic table, 8, 72

Grubbs catalysts, 72–73

Gschneidner, Karl A., Jr., 153

Guillaume, Charles Édouard, 57

H

haemocyanin, 59

haemoglobin, 52

hafnium, 82–83

Hahn, Otto, 171

Hall, Charles, 102–3

halogens, 192–203

hatter's shakes, 99

helium, 206–7

Héroult, Paul, 102–3

Hevesy, Georg Karl von, 82, 90

Hiroshima, 172–73

holmium, 154–55

hydrogen, 10–11, 76–77

I

implants, 45, 84

indium, 106–7

inert gases. *See* noble gases

infrared light absorption, 156

Invar, 56–57

iodine, 129, 193, 200–201

ionic mimicry,
34, 81, 107, 111, 149

iridium, 90, 92–93

iron, 52–53, 73, 136–37

isotopes, 69, 170–71, 181

J

James, Charles, 162

jewellery, 94, 97

K

Kean, Sam, 105

kilogram standard, 93

Kirchoff, Gustav R., 20, 22

Klaproth, Martin Heinrich,
64, 148–49, 172

kohl, 126–27

krypton, 212–13

L

LaBa dating, 135

Lamy, Claude-Auguste, 110

lanthanoids, 62, 132–63

lanthanum, 134–35

Large Hadron Collider
(LHC), 67

lasers, 141, 155

Le Mans disaster, 30–31

lead, 49, 68, 106, 112–13, 127

Lecoq de Boisbaudran,
Paul-Émile (François),
104–5, 146, 152–53

lenses, 123, 135, 139, 157

lethal injections, 19

Li, Tianle, 111

Libby, Willard, 181

lighting
fluorescent, 29, 211
gas lamps, 169
incandescent bulbs, 86, 91
metal halide lamps, 153, 159
natural sunlight bulbs, 43
neon lights, 205, 209
sodium lights, 17

limescale, 33

lithium, 12–13, 14–15

Litvinenko, Alexander, 131

luminous paint, 38–39, 143

lutetium, 162–63

M

magnesium, 26–27, 30–31

magnetism, 53, 66–67,
140–41, 145, 155, 157

magnetostriction, 151

manganese, 50–51

Marignac, Jean Charles Galissard de, 149, 160

Marsh test, 125

medical uses
  antiseptic, 200–201
  burns treatment, 137
  cancer treatment, 95, 97, 166–67
  historic uses, 39, 79, 124, 198–99
  imaging, 37, 67, 71, 149, 155
  implants, 45, 84
  laser treatment, 155
  mental health, 14
  neurology, 140–41
  radioactivity, 39, 71, 97, 166–67
  stomach ailments, 115

Meitner, Lise, 171

Mendeleev, Dmitri, 6, 7, 42, 43, 88, 104–5, 122–23, 129

mercury, 98–99

metalloids, 116–31

metre standard, 213

mimicry, ionic, 34, 81, 107, 111, 149

Minamata Convention, 99

mirrors, 74, 78, 107

mischmetals, 134–35, 136–37

Moissan, Henri, 87, 194

molybdenum, 68–69

Mosander, Carl Gustaf, 134, 138, 150

Moseley, Henry, 6, 7–8, 82, 129

MRI (magnetic resonance imaging), 67, 149, 155

N

Nagasaki, 174–75

naming of elements, 144–45, 176–77

Napoleonic army, 109

neodymium, 138–39, 140–41

neon, 208–9

neutrons, 29

nickel, 56–57

niobium, 66–67

nitrogen, 182–83

noble gases, 204–17

Noddack, Walter & Ida, 71, 88

non-metals, 178–91

nuclear disasters, 23, 35, 201

nuclear reactors, 83, 119, 145, 147, 169, 175

nuclear weapons, 29, 172–73, 174–75

O

Oak Ridge National Laboratory (ORNL), 143

oganesson, 8, 145, 216

oil industry, 36, 43

optical clocks, 161

optical fibres, 157

osmium, 90–91, 92

oxidation, 185, 193

oxidation states, 88, 93, 146, 160–61

oxygen, 184–85

ozone, 185, 195

P

palladium, 76–77

paper thickness gauges, 143

Perey, Marguerite, 25

periodic table
  groups, 8, 72
  history, 6–8, 42, 104, 122–23, 129, 202, 210–11
  periods, 8–9

Perrier, Carlo, 70

pesticides, 199

pewter, 113

philosopher's stone, 186–87, 188

phosphorescence, 146

phosphors, 151

phosphorus, 186–87

photography, 79, 123, 135

photosynthesis, 147

pigments, 45, 49, 54, 98, 124, 137, 173

plants, 19, 31, 147, 183, 191

platinum, 93, 94–95

platinum group, 72

plutonium, 174–75

poisons. See toxicity

polonium, 130–31

Pons, Stanley, 77

poor metals, 100–115

postage stamps, 147

post-transition metals, 100–115

potassium, 12–13, 18 19, 111

praseodymium, 138–39

Priestley, Joseph, 184

promethium, 142–43

protactinium, 170–71

pyrite, 53

pyrophoric materials, 136

Q

quartz thermometers, 105

R

radiation protection, 113

radioactive Boy Scout, 169

radioactive elements
  actinoids, 164–77
  carbon-14, 181
  luminous paint, 38–39, 143
  medical uses, 71, 97, 166–67
  nuclear bombs, 172–73, 174–75
  nuclear fuel, 169, 172–73, 175
  scandium-46 as tracer, 43
  short-lived, 25, 143, 171
  toxicity, 23, 34–35, 38–39, 55, 130–31, 168–69, 201, 217

Radithor, 168–69

radium, 26–27, 38–39, 167

radon, 216–17

Ramsay, William, 205, 206, 208–9, 211, 212–13, 214, 217

rare earths. *See* lanthanoids

Rayleigh, John William Strutt, 3rd Baron, 210–11

reactivity, 13, 195

recycling, 31

redox reactions, 61, 160–61

Reich, Ferdinand, 106

rhenium, 88–89

rhodium, 74–75

Richter, Hieronymus Theodor, 106

rubber, 129

rubidium, 12–13, 20–21

rust, 53, 185

ruthenium, 72–73

Rutherford, Daniel, 182

sacrificial metals, 31, 61

samarium, 144–45

sand, 120

scandium, 42–43

Scheele, Carl Wilhelm, 68, 86–87, 184, 196

Scott's Antarctic expedition, 109

Seaborg, Glenn, 8, 177

seaborgium, 8, 145

Sefström, Nils, 46

Segrè, Emilio, 70, 203

selenium, 179, 190–91

semiconductors, 121, 123, 124

semimetals. *See* metalloids

shape-memory metals, 57

silicon, 120–21

silicones, 121

silver, 78–79

single molecule magnets (SMMs), 157

sodium, 12–13, 16–17

solder, 113

Soret, Jacques-Louis, 154–55

spacecraft, 15, 215

Spedding, Frank, 153

stainless steel, 48

standard measurements, 22–23, 93, 213

steel, 47, 48, 61, 69, 119

Stromeyer, Friedrich, 80

strontium, 26–27, 34–35

sulfur, 188–89

superconductors, 63, 66–67

syphilis, 124

Tacke, Ida, 71, 88

tantalum, 84–85

tarnish, 79, 185

technetium, 69, 70–71, 88

teeth, 34–35, 51, 195

tellurium, 128–29

Tennant, Smithson, 90, 92, 180

terbium, 150–51

thallium, 110–11

thermal expansion, 56–57, 65

thermometers, quartz, 105

thorium, 168–69, 171

thulium, 158–59

time measurement, 22–23, 161

tin, 108–9, 113

titanium, 44–45

TNT (trinitrotoluene), 183

toothpaste, 109

toxicity

 arsenic, 124–25

 barium, 37

 beryllium, 28–29

 halogens, 194, 196–97, 201

 heavy metals, 49, 55, 80–81, 98–99, 110–11, 112–13

 mimics, 34–35, 80–81, 111, 149, 158

osmium tetroxide, 91

 radioactive elements, 23, 34–35, 38–39, 55, 130–31, 168–69, 201, 217

 selenium, 191

 white phosphorus, 187

transition metals, 40–99

Travers, Morris William, 205, 208–9, 212–13, 214

tungsten, 86–87, 91

uranium, 171, 172–73

vanadium, 46–47

VCM (vinyl chloride monomer), 99

von Reichenstein, Franz-Joseph Müller, 128

vulcanization, 129

watch springs, 57

water, hard, 33

water treatment, 135, 197

weapons

 chemical, 65, 187, 196–97

 guns, 43

 nuclear, 29, 172–73, 174–75

weighting agents, 36

Welsbach, Auer von, 162–63

Wollaston, William Hyde, 74, 76

Wood's metal, 114–15

xenon, 214–15

X-rays, 37, 159

ytterbium, 160–61

yttrium, 62–63, 148

zinc, 60–61, 80, 107

zirconium, 64–65, 82

Credits

Alamy Stock Photo
54: Science Photo Library; 113: Susan E. Degginger; 115 (bottom): D. Hurst; 131: Photo 12; 139 (left): Zoonar GmbH; 141 (bottom): PHOTOTAKE Inc.; 145 (top): ZUMA Press, Inc.; 193: sciencephotos; 203: Randsc

Creative Commons
5, 72: Metalle-w; 10: ESA/Hubble; 15 (top): Steve Jervetson; 16 (bottom): Dennıs 'S. K' (Dnn87); 28 (top): Yolc Rosen/ Dr. Mark Wick; 39 (bottom): Arma95; 44: Cory W. Watts; 50, 129 (top), 144: Rob Lavinsky/iRocks.com; 42, 57 (top), 60, 147 (top), 158, 205: Alchemist-hp; 59 (bottom): DanCentury; 62: Krizu; 67 (top): CERN; 67 (bottom) NobbiP; 75: Kristian Molhave; 88: Dome_de; 89: David Monniaux; 90: Alexander C. Wimmer; 91 (bottom): Periodictableru; 94 (bottom): Sailko; 97: Ondrej Martin Mach; 104: Thomas Nguyen; 106, 111, 122 (top), 150, 151 (right), 152, 190: http://images-of-elements. com; 112: Andrew Dunn/www.andrewdunnphoto.com; 117 (top): James St. John; 125 (bottom): Ji-Elle; 127 (top): © Jorge Royan/http://www.royan.com.ar/CC BY-SA 3.0; 127 (bottom): WillisPThomas; 135, 148, 163, 210 (bottom): Jurii; 136: AkselA; 139 (right): Spidey71; 142: Geomartin; 154: Benoît Derrier; 157: Ximeg; 169 (top): Sam L.; 170: Energy.gov; 181 (right): Jochen Gschnaller; 191: Stan Shebs; 200 (right): Danny S.; 209 (top): Jan Homann

Getty Images
18, 200 (left): © Philip Evans; 63: Peter Ginter; 71: Zephyr/ Science Photo Library; 108: DEA Picture Library; 129 (bottom): Keystone-France; 189 (bottom): De Agostini Picture Library

Science Photo Library
20: Emilio Segre Visual Archives/American Institute of Physics; 22, 213 (bottom): National Physical Laboratory © Crown Copyright; 25: American Institute of Physics; 77: Philippe Plailly; 81: Biophoto Associates; 95: Dr. P. Marazzi; 105 GIPhotoStock; 153 (top): Iowa State University/ American Institute of Physics; 161: Andrew Brookes/National Physical Laboratory; 175: Patrick Landmann/ Science Photo Library; 147: Science Photo Library; 217 (bottom): Public Health England

Shutterstock
4, 114: Jiri Vaclavek; 11, 99, 173 (top), 174 (top and bottom): Everett Historical; 13, 64 (top), 80, 98: Albert Russ; 14 Imfoto; 15 (bottom): design 56; 17: Gary James Calder; 19: Oscity; 23: Bychykhin Olexandr; 27: totojang1977; 28 (bottom): Nastya22; 31: Tethys Imaging LLC; 32: Tortoon; 33: Vladimir Mucibabic; 36: Amineah; 37: thailoei92; 41: Namthip Muanthongthae; 43: Piotr Zajc; 45 (top): Tushchakorn; 45 (bottom): Daniela Pelazza; 47 (bottom): Lorerock81; 49: Don Pablo; 51 (top): Baciu; 51 (bottom): Imageman; 52 (top): wacomka; 52 (bottom): Denis Radovanovic; 53: revers; 55 bluecrayola; 56: Daniel D Malone; 57 (bottom): Alexey Kamenskiy; 58: dibrova; 59 (top): Coprid; 61: Sarin Kunthong; 64 (bottom): sebra; 69: bonchan; 73: NV77; 74: Adam J; 78: 5 Second Studio; 79 (top): In Green; 82: S-F; 83: VPales; 84: Greentea Latte; 85: Nada B; 86: Evannovostro; 87: Jason Dudley; 92: Ti Santi; 94 (top) Kirill Smirnov; 99 (top): MarcelClemens; 101 (top): yanisa nithichananthorn; 101 (bottom): tcsaba; 102 (left): showcake; 102 (right): AlenKadr; 103: Yulia Grigoryeva; 107: kyokyo; 109: pryzmat; 115 (top): milezaway; 118: Richard Thornton; 120: Edward Westmacott; 121 (top): Kuchina; 121 (bottom): dsmsoft; 123: mozakim; 133: Film Factory; 137 (top): iceink; 140: NikolayN; 141 (top): iradet Ponari; 145 (bottom): tam_odin; 149: AkeSak; 151 (left): GalapagosPhoto; 153 (bottom): dumbell619; 155: Suttha Burawonk; 159: Syda Productions; 165: SpaceKris; 173 (bottom): Margrit Hirsch; 179 (top): Rat007; 179 (bottom left): Tyler Boyes; 179 (bottom right): gualtiero boffi; 180 (top): elina; 180 (bottom): watin; 181 (left): Comaniciu Dan; 183 (top): Joy Tasa; 183 (bottom): testing; 185 (top): studio23; 185 (bottom): wk1003mike; 187 (bottom): ilolab; 188: littlew00dy; 189 (top): SIAATH; 195 (top): Joseph Sohm; 195 (bottom): Mau Horng; 197 (bottom): posteriori; 199 (bottom): Mike Flippo; 201: jiangdi; 207 (top): pukach; 208: Neil Lang; 211: Posonskyi Andrey; 214: Sunny_Images

Wellcome Library, London
38, 76, 96, 110, 119, 124, 125 (top);126 (bottom): Science Museum, London; 130 (bottom), 168, 176, 184, 186, 194 (bottom), 196, 199 (top), 209 (boxout), 211 (top), 217 (top)

Misc.
21: NIST/JILA/CU-Boulder; 29: Los Alamos National Laboratory*; 35 (bottom): Associated Press